DETROIT PUBLIC LIBRARY

D1255142

DRAKE

Some other books by Jean Lee Latham

YOUNG MAN IN A HURRY

ON STAGE, MR. JEFFERSON!

THIS DEAR-BOUGHT LAND

CARRY ON, MR. BOWDITCH

TRAIL BLAZER OF THE SEAS

DRAKE

The Man They Called a Pirate

BY JEAN LEE LATHAM

WINNER OF THE 1955 NEWBERY AWARD

illustrated by Frederick T. Chapman

HARPER & BROTHERS · *Publishers*
New York

DRAKE

Printed in the United States of America

C-K

Library of Congress catalog card number: 60-5784

To

my guides, philosophers, and friends
at the University of Miami

George AND *Madeline*
who lead me through library labyrinths

Mel
who monitors maritime matters

J. L. L.

DRAKE

1

Wanted—a master mariner

His eyes snapped open and Fran stared, surprised, into darkness. What in the world had wakened him? He lifted himself on one elbow and held his breath to listen. Silence . . . then the scuffle of cautious footsteps, a muttered curse when someone stumbled, and a piercing "Shhh!"

Robbers? If they were, they were certainly strangers. Any sailor around the Medway knew there was nothing worth stealing on the *Clarissa*. When Fran called her "my father's ship" the sailors always laughed. "*Ship?* That worm-eaten hulk hasn't been to sea since the days of Henry the Eighth!"

The scuffle faded as the prowlers went aft. Fran slid out of his bunk, moving quietly so he would not waken his little brothers.

Johnny stirred and whispered, "Fran? Did you hear it?"

"Just some prowlers. I'll take care of them."

Johnny's teeth were chattering. "Wh-what are you going to do?"

"I don't know yet. But something. When you hear a yell, and then a splash, that'll be the pair of them jumping overboard."

"D-do you need me to help you?"

"No. There's only two of them—I think."

Johnny heaved a sigh of relief. "I'd come if you needed me."

"Sure you would. You stay here with the little ones. When the racket starts, they might be scared."

He tiptoed from the fo'c'sle, started aft, stumbled against something in the dark, and smothered an "Ouch!" One of the kegs Mother grew flowers in. Poor Mother, it must be hard for a woman to have to live on a ship. If Mother had her way, he thought, we'd thatch the fo'c'sle and poop, and plant a garden on the quarter-deck. He grinned. He'd tell the boys that when he got back if the noise had wakened them. Start them giggling, and they'd get over being scared.

He tiptoed a few steps farther, paused in the shadows, and held his breath to listen. He heard his father's voice.

"Yes, Ben? What is it?"

Only some sailors come to talk to Father. Funny time of the night to bother him. If they wakened Mother, she'd really shake her head over this. Just the other evening, when Father came aboard very late, she said, "Dear, you're supposed to read prayers to the fleet morning and evening. Do you have to spend all day, every day, answering the sailors' questions?"

And now—here they were in the middle of the night. Fran shrugged and started back to his bunk.

"We came to warn you, Mr. Drake," Ben said. "It ain't going to be safe for you to read prayers to us no more."

Fran wheeled and stood motionless in the shadows.

Father sounded impatient. "Bah! I'm not afraid of Queen Mary and her—"

Big Hugh Morrow's voice rumbled, "Not safe for you to read prayers, and not safe for us to listen."

"Oh . . ." After a time Father added, "I hadn't thought of that."

"We have," Hugh growled. "Bloody Mary had two men burned at the stake yesterday in Kent. Not twenty miles from here. That's getting too close for comfort. You've got to clear out of here, Mr. Drake. We came to help you get away before—"

"I've nowhere to go," Father said. "I'm safer here than back in Devon. And at least the *Clarissa* is a roof over our heads."

"What'll you do without a job?" Ben asked. "How'll you feed all your young ones?"

"Work around the dockyards, I suppose. The Queen can't object to that, can she?"

"Not if you keep your tongue between your teeth," Hugh suggested. "But you'll have a time feeding that tribe of boys. Remember what my old gram used to say. 'A growing boy has a wolf in his belly.' Too bad they're so young. If you could just prentice them to ship masters—"

"No! I went through that when I was a lad. Working until I was so tired I slept on my feet. Wet to the skin night and day for a week at a time. Before I married I handed my last sail. I promised my wife I'd never send a son to sea."

"Things were different then," Hugh said.

"Times will get better," Father insisted.

Old Ben snorted. "I've heard that before! England's been going downhill ever since King Henry died. How old's your biggest boy?"

"Fran's ten. And he's going to make a name for himself. I tell you, he's smart as a whip. He could read before he was—"

"Sure, sure!" Ben agreed. "Mighty fine lad. Prentice him to a master mariner—one that can really train him—and he'll go right to the top. Some day he might be Captain Francis Drake! With his own ship! How's that sound? Captain Francis Drake?"

A prickle chased over Fran's scalp and down his back. He straightened and stood, feet wide, arms folded, chin up.

Father spoke slowly. "Yes, he'd probably get to the top. But I know what he'd go through getting there. He's going to have a better life than that."

"How?" Hugh asked. "How'll you educate him? Better

send him to sea. At least you'll have one less mouth to feed."

"That's enough!" Father snapped. "Good night!"

Long after the men had gone Fran stood alone in the shadows. The moon rose from the mist of the North Sea and sent its glow up the mouth of the Thames and into the Medway River. He watched the silver light outline the masts and spars of the ships anchored in the Medway—high-built ships of England's navy—low, squatty coasters—little fishing vessels.

"I wonder," he whispered, "which one has a master mariner?"

Behind him someone spoke. "Fran? You all right?" He jumped and turned.

Johnny stood there, big-eyed, shaking, clutching a chunk of wood that must have weighed half as much as he did. "I know you said to stay with the little ones. But I waited and waited. I had to come to help you."

"I'm sorry I was so long. It was just some men to see Father."

"Oh . . ." Johnny let the wood *thunk* to the deck. "Too bad it wasn't prowlers. Been fun to hear them yell and jump." He managed a shaky giggle, but it didn't last long. "I *had* to come to help you, Fran. If anything happened to you we'd never have any more fun."

I'd better tell him now, Fran thought. Give him time to get used to the idea. "Look, Johnny . . ."

Johnny listened, gulped, and wet his lips. "How long does a prentice serve?"

"Seven years, I think."

"*Seven years!* But we'll be grown up in seven years! I'll be fifteen and Joe'll be thirteen and—we won't ever have any more fun together. We—" He turned and stood with his back to Fran. "It's going to be awful for the little ones without their b-big b-brother."

"You'll be 'big brother' after I'm gone."

"It won't be the same," Johnny whispered. "Even little Tommy likes you best. When he's hollering and you pick him up, he stops in the middle of a yell and grabs a handful of your hair and starts laughing."

There was a lump in Fran's throat now. "Tommy won't remember me very long." He knew Johnny was crying. He kept talking, to give him a chance to get over it. "If Tommy won't grab your hair, try him on Joe's. It's more like mine, huh?"

At last Johnny ducked his head and swiped at his cheeks with the backs of his hands. "How soon will you have to go?"

"Soon as I find the right ship. One with a master mariner."

"How'll you know which ship?"

"I'll ask around. The sailors are used to me asking questions. They won't catch on to anything."

"A master mariner, eh?" The sailor stared across the water. "Best mariner that's in the Medway right now? I'd say Adam Tanner. Old fellow. Must be seventy. Mighty old for a sailor. Know why I think he's lasted so long? He's so low-down mean that even Old Nick doesn't want him. That's his ship over there—the *Sally.*"

Fran looked. "That little coaster? With only one mast?"

The sailor nodded. "One mast, two sails, rigged fore-and-aft. Good rig for a coaster. A small crew can handle her. Don't believe Tanner has more than two men with him now. Sometimes he carries three. One fellow must have jumped ship. Don't blame him. That Tanner's the meanest old devil that ever walked a deck. But, man alive, he's a mariner! I've heard men say . . ."

Ten minutes later Fran stood on the wharf by the little coaster. A huge man with a black beard was singing a cheerful song in a foreign tongue and handling casks and barrels as easily as Fran would lift a mug of water. A short, squat man with pale red hair worked silently and sweated.

"Aboard the *Sally!*" Fran called.

The song stopped. White teeth gleamed through the big man's black beard. "*Buenos días, señor!*"

The red-haired man glanced up, but did not speak. His wide, thin mouth turned down in a sour smile. He shrugged and went on with his work.

The red-head looks like a bad-tempered fish, Fran thought. I like the big fellow better, even if he is a foreigner.

Then someone snarled, "What the devil do you want?"

Fran looked toward the stern of the ship and saw a small, wiry, weather-beaten man with a short gray beard and black eyes that peered out from the bristling ambush of his eyebrows.

Fran saluted. "Master Tanner, I request permission to come aboard, sir."

The old man nodded. When Fran stood before him he said, "Well?"

"Do you have a berth for another man on the *Sally*, sir?"

"Why?"

"I'd like to sign on as a prentice, sir."

"Hah! Runaway, aren't you? And mighty far from home!"

"I live right here on the Medway, sir."

"How come you speak with the tongue of a Devon man?"

"My family came from there. A long time ago. I don't remember about it. I was just a child then. Only four."

"How old are you now?"

Instead of answering Fran stepped forward, flexing his right arm. "Feel that, Master Tanner."

Adam's fist blurred. Fran landed halfway across the deck. Adam followed and stood looking down at him. "When I ask a question I want an answer. How old are you?"

Fran got up, shook his head groggily, and straightened. "Almost eleven, sir. And I'm strong for my size."

"What's your name?"

"Drake, sir."

"Oh . . . One of that tribe. Your father reads prayers to the fleet."

"He did. But he's losing his job, sir."

"Lucky if he doesn't lose his life," Adam said, "with Bloody Mary on the throne. You know how many Englishmen she's had burned at the stake? Since she married Philip of Spain?"

"No, sir. I just know my father has to have help. That's why I'm going to sea. He'll have one less mouth to feed."

"Well, well! That'll be just fine—for your father. But how'd you help me? What'd you do to make you worth your hardtack and bully beef? Can you heave a lead and take soundings?"

"No, sir, not yet, but—"

"Can you shoot the sun and work your latitude?"

"No, sir, but—"

"Do you know the shape of every headland and bit of coast on the Channel? Can you figure the time of high tide at any harbor any day of the year? Well?"

"No, sir, I don't know any of those things—yet."

"Then why the devil should I sign you on?"

"I could learn, sir. If I sailed with you, I'd learn a lot. Men say 'Old—' Men say 'Master Tanner has wrung more salt water out of his shirt than most of us have sailed over.' "

"What else do they say?"

Fran hesitated, then looked squarely into the old man's eyes. "That you are 'the meanest old devil that ever walked a deck.' "

Adam nodded. "That's more like it! When I ask a question I want an answer. Don't ever forget it."

"No, sir!" Fran grinned. "You'll sign me on?"

"No, I won't sign you on! Get off my ship and stay off! I catch you around here again, I'll keelrake you!" And Adam strode forward to bellow at his men. "Pedro! Carey! Bear a hand! We're going out in the morning!"

Fran stood a moment, studying the *Sally*. He looked longest at some cargo, lashed to the deck and covered with a tarpaulin. He nodded to himself, saluted Adam Tanner's back, and left the ship.

At dawn the *Sally* went out with the turn of the tide. At the helm Adam Tanner flicked a glance about him, checking mast, sails, and rigging.

Pedro nudged the red-headed man. "Behold, Carey! Master Tanner can find nothing wrong! Poor *señor!* He will be sad all day."

Carey shrugged and his mouth turned down in its sour smile.

Then one corner of a tarpaulin lashed over cargo on deck flapped in the breeze. Adam brightened and began to roar. What fool had secured that tarp with a lubber's knot? He called them everything he could lay his tongue to, including "gallows bait."

2

The dream of a drum

The *Sally* had cleared the Thames and was standing to the south close-hauled when Fran eeled out of his hiding place.

Pedro was at the helm. "*Por Dios!* The little *señor!* You want to get killed? Where the devil am I going to hide you?"

"Nowhere. I'm going to report to Master Tanner." He took a deep breath, stiffened, and marched aft.

In his cabin Adam half rose from his chair. "So you didn't believe what I said, eh? Maybe you've never seen a man keelraked?"

"Yes, sir, I did. Once."

"What happened to him?"

"They tied his hands together behind him. They tied another rope around his ankles. They threw him overboard and dragged him under the ship."

"What'd he look like when they brought him up?"

"His clothes were mostly torn off him. The barnacles,

I guess. He was cut and bleeding all over."

"Well?"

"After you get done keelraking me, sir, I'm going to work hard for you. If you'll sign me on as a prentice I'll work hard for you seven years, sir. Because I know I'll learn a lot. Some day I'll know how to heave a lead and take soundings and how to shoot the sun and work my latitude. I'll know the shape of every headland and bit of coast on the Channel. I'll know how to figure the time of high tide at any harbor any day of the year."

Adam sank back in his chair. His jaw dropped. "Word for word . . . Well, I'll be . . ." He bristled. "But what do you know now? Is the weather side of a ship to starboard or larboard?"

"Either one. It's the side the wind's coming from."

"Humph." Adam looked glum. "What's the standing rigging?"

"The ropes that hold the masts steady."

Adam brightened. "*Lines!* Not *ropes,* you fool!"

"Yes, sir, *lines.*"

"What's the running rigging?"

"The—uh—*lines* that move things."

"Humph. If you're on a square-rigger, where do you stand to furl a tops'l?"

"On the—uh—foot line."

"*Rope!* Not *line,* you half-wit!"

"Yes, sir. *Rope.*"

For half an hour Adam hammered questions and bellowed corrections. At last he said, "Well, now that you're here, I might as well sign you on—for this trip." He shoved a book toward Fran. "Make your mark."

"May I sign my name, sir?"

"You can write?"

"Yes, sir. My father taught me." Under Pedro's scrawl and Carey's X he wrote, "F. Drake."

"Any good at arithmetic?"

"Yes, sir. I like it."

"Hmmm." Adam's fingers drummed on the book. "I've never signed on a prentice, but you might do. We'll talk about that when we put into the Medway again—if you still think you want to serve under me. It's my guess you won't."

"Yes, sir. When will we put into the Medway, sir?"

"Now that's a fool's question if I ever heard one! Who knows? I pick up cargoes where I can, and take them where they're bound for—God willing and the winds with me. With a fair wind we make three–four knots. When we're windbound, we wait. When we're becalmed, we sit there and rot." He stood. "Well, that's enough of that."

"Yes, sir." Fran clenched his fists and pressed them hard against his thighs. "About the keelraking, sir . . ."

"Well?"

"These are the only clothes I have. Could I take them off before you throw me overboard?"

"Hmmm." Adam's gnarled hand rasped across his

beard. "Well, I tell you, Drake, I never keelrake a man till I'm in port and ready to discharge him. I get the good out of him first."

"Yes, sir." Fran bit his lips.

"Scared, were you?"

Fran nodded.

"But you came aboard anyhow?"

"Yes, sir."

"Hmmm. You know, Drake, I just might make a mariner out of you. A master mariner! You'll need to know your trade. There's a lot to learn. But you know what a master needs above everything? Courage! The sea is a devil, Drake. It'll take everything you've got to stand up to her. And a master—he has to have courage enough for himself and every man on his crew. Pouring courage into your men—sometimes it's like pouring water down a rat hole."

For the first weeks homesickness and hunger for sleep were the worst of it. Worse than the cold that numbed his hands, the cracks that bled, scabbed over, split and bled again. Worse than his terror when a wave crashed over the deck, swept him off his feet, and smashed him into the scuppers.

He could have stood anything, he thought, with enough sleep. But his head swam, his eyeballs felt dry, and every joint in his body felt as though it needed grease.

In the daytime, even when he was off watch, he never had a chance to sleep. Any free moment Adam was after him with problems to solve and facts to memorize. Was there no end to what a mariner needed to know?

Every few days Adam grilled him:

"What does a ship do when she pitches?"

"She rocks on her middle, plunging first her head and then her stern into the sea."

"What can you do to prevent pitching?"

"You have to know your ship. How she carries sail. How high or low to stow the heaviest part of your cargo."

"How do you come to anchor in a square-rigger if you're scudding under a for's'l?"

"You must clew up the sail before you come to your berth and run part of the way under bare poles. At the right time you put the helm hard alee. Then, at the right time, you let go an anchor, and make sure you give her enough cable."

"Humph," Adam growled, "you can spout it, all right. But how'll you know *when* to clew up your for's'l, and *when* to put your helm hard alee, and *when* to let go the anchor? Eh?"

Fran had no answer to that. He just knew his head was swimming with all the facts he must learn:

"Name every port on the Channel from Falmouth to Dover."

"Draw me a chart of Plymouth Harbor."

"What kind of soundings will your dipsey lead bring up as you make the Lizard from the east?"

"Chart me the currents off Le Havre, four hours after high tide at Dover."

"How would you steer your ship if her rudder was lost?"

"Name the thirty-two points of the compass."

One day when Fran had managed to get through an hour's grilling without a mistake—and Adam was looking glum—the old man asked, "How you get along with Pedro?"

"Just fine, sir. I like him. I'm helping him with his English."

"You picking up any Spanish from him?"

"Why . . . no, sir."

Adam brightened. "Well, well! And why not?"

"But I'm English! Why would I want to learn foreign jabber?"

"Oh, so you're English! Tell me—do you ever expect to sail beyond the Channel?"

"Yes, sir. Some day I'll command my own ship, sir, sailing to far-off ports."

"Then you'd better learn every scrap of 'foreign jabber' you can. You know why? Because the only place in the world where your precious English is spoken is on our one little island. Go anywhere else in the world, *you'll* be the one that's talking 'foreign jabber.' "

"Oh . . . Could I get Pedro to teach me some Spanish?"

"Easy. Point to things and say 'kay ess?' That means

'what is?' If he goes too fast yell 'kah-RRRRAHM-bah!' "

"Is that swearing, sir?"

"Why?"

"My family doesn't think much of swearing, sir."

"Humph. And you're going to command your own ship to far-off ports, are you? I'd like to live long enough to hear you do that—without swearing."

"Why, sir?"

"The gallows bait in the fo'c'sle don't understand any other language. If you want them to hop fast you—"

"When I yell, they'll hop," Fran said. "Will I be swearing if I yell 'kah-RRRRAHM-bah'?"

"Absolutely not!"

After that, when Fran had weathered a grilling without a mistake, Adam switched to questions in Spanish until Fran had to say, "I don't know, sir." It seemed to brighten Adam's day.

Two months—three—four. The ache for sleep was not quite so bad, but the ache for home was still there. Just to have his brothers listening, wide-eyed, to what he said —to pick up little Tommy when he hollered—to hear Mother say "You're a big help, Fran"—to feel Father's hand on his shoulder. When, oh, when would he see home again? No use to ask Adam, but maybe Pedro . . .

Pedro smiled and shrugged. "The Medway? Who knows?"

Three months later Pedro smiled and shrugged again.

"Two times I have heard Master Tanner refuse a cargo for the Medway. Maybe we not ever go there any more."

Two years passed before the *Sally* put into the Medway, with the bellow of Adam Tanner running before her. They came to anchor within sight of the *Clarissa.*

Fran stared hungrily across the water. He saw his father, stoop-shouldered, shuffling across the deck. A tall, fair-haired boy—could that be Johnny? Had he strung up that fast in two years? And the short, sturdily built one with a mop of dark red hair . . . That must be Joe, Fran thought. Father always said he looked like me.

"Well, Drake," Adam asked, "how you feel about a prenticeship under me now? Had enough?"

I've already served two years, Fran told himself. I can last five more! He said, "It suits me fine, Master Tanner. I've learned a lot."

"Humph. You haven't scratched the surface. Well, we'll go talk to your father. See what he has to say. I'll not bother with a prentice unless your father signs the paper, and unless *you* give your word that you won't go back on your bargain!"

Fran blazed. "I don't break promises—sir!"

Adam studied his right fist. "No . . . Don't want to take you home with a black eye. Save that for later. Come along."

"Aye, aye, sir. Uh—Master Tanner, there's one thing. Like I said, they don't think much of swearing. And if you—uh—shouted at Mother, she'd say 'no.' And Father would have to stand by her. You see, he promised her he'd never send a son to sea. So, in a way, it's Mother we've got to convince."

"Women! Don't ever get married, Drake. Seafaring and home life don't mix. Come on. We'll see what your *mother* has to say!"

Fran had a chance to whisper only one thing to his mother as he hugged her. "Remember! I've already served two years!"

Then they were all sitting on benches around the plank table—Father with bowed head and troubled face, Johnny big-eyed and solemn, eight-year-old Joe beaming with excitement, and the younger boys staring silently at this brother they did not remember.

Mother twisted her hands together. "Master Tanner, I lost two brothers at sea. I saw another come home so sick he died in a month. I swore my boys would never be sailors."

Fran watched Adam conquer his bellow before he spoke. "Madam, can you think of a better future for him right now? A pauper—and a Protestant? It's my guess he's safer out of the country than in it. As long as Bloody Mary and Philip of Spain—"

"If Queen Mary dies without children," Mother said, "Elizabeth will be queen. And we'll be rid of Philip of Spain."

"Will we, Madam?" Adam picked up an apple and a knife. "Let this apple be the world, Madam." He pricked a dot on it. "That's England." He slashed the apple in two and held up one-half of it. "And here is the half of the world that belongs to Philip of Spain. All the lands not already ruled by Christian princes. Philip has more territory, more riches, and more power than any ruler since Caesar. He landed on our shores once as a bridegroom. Next time he might come as a conqueror."

"But we have the sea to protect us!" Mother said.

Adam started to roar, paused, and spoke quietly again. "A sea is no protection without a navy, Madam. And we've let our navy go to rack and ruin. Do you know how many ships we had when Henry was king?"

Mother stiffened. "I don't know anything about his ships. But I think Henry the Eighth was a dreadful man. All those poor women he married and—"

This time Adam forgot about not roaring. He was on his feet, shouting. "Madam! We'll leave his private life out of this! I'm talking about his navy! Dozens of ships! Well-built! Seaworthy! And manned by real mariners! When I sailed with the Portsmouth fleet, do you know what our watchword was? 'God save the King!' And the answer was, 'Long to reign over us!' That's what we thought of Henry the Eighth! Listen to me, Madam! . . ."

Adam talked on and on. Finally he leaned forward, hands flat on the table. "Madam, if ever England holds up her head again, it will be because of her mariners! And you whimper about a hard life at sea! What'd be so easy about life under the heel of a conqueror? And don't think

England couldn't be invaded! Because we could be! Unless our mariners save us!"

At last Father signed the paper.

"He's so young!" Mother pleaded. "You'll be easy on him, won't you?"

"No, Madam. That wouldn't prepare him to be a master of the sea. But I'll teach him all I can—if he doesn't give up some day and jump ship."

Fran leaped to his feet, then got a grip on himself. "I won't go back on my bargain, sir. You have my word."

"You may stay with your family tonight, Drake. Report tomorrow morning. Early."

"Aye, aye, sir."

"Thank goodness," Mother said, "he has only five more years."

"So?" Adam came as near smiling as he ever did. "Madam, he promised to serve for seven years. This paper is dated today—October fourteen, fifteen fifty-seven. He will serve until October fourteen, fifteen sixty-four."

"But he's already been a prentice for two years!"

"No, Madam. He wasn't a prentice then. Just a poor little runaway that I befriended. A poor little runaway that I took to my heart and cared for like a father." Adam slapped the paper across his hand. "Seven years, Drake!" He strode out.

"Why, that—that—creature!" Mother gasped. "He tricked you!"

"I tricked him first," Fran said, "when I hid on the *Sally*."

"But seven more years!"

"Probably take that long for me to learn all I need to know," Fran said. "The sea is a devil."

"Francis Drake! We'll have no swearing in this home!"

Father smiled faintly. "That was not really swearing, dear. Just a statement of fact." He looked at Fran and his smile faded. "I wish I could have done more for you, lad. You deserve a better chance."

"I've got a chance. To be a master mariner."

That night he dreamed he was on his own ship sailing to far-off ports. He motioned to his drummer and the rat-a-tat-tat called all hands on deck. Hundreds of men swarmed topside and stood at attention, looking at him, their captain! Ready to obey his commands!

The next morning he reported back to the *Sally*. Adam began snarling orders again.

3

The taste of command

A year later, November of 1558, they put into the Medway in the midst of a wild celebration. Bells ringing, guns booming, people shouting. Bloody Mary was dead! Elizabeth was queen!

"God help England," Adam said. "Another woman on the throne. And God help Elizabeth. She's taking charge of a foundering ship in a rising gale." He cocked a glance at Fran. "Well, Drake, guess your father will be better off now. Probably get a vicarage. Be able to feed his tribe. How about it? If I let you go to see your family, think you'll come back?"

Fran tried to fight down the red haze of his fury, but he yelled, "You have my word, confound you!"

He reported home with a puffy eye. He hoped nobody would notice it, but Joe grinned and spit on his fist.

Then Mother saw the eye. "Fran!" she pleaded. "You don't have to go through that any longer."

"I've given my word."

"But it's so foolish! If you're determined to be a sailor, you could sign on with your cousins in Plymouth. John and William Hawkins. They have the finest merchant fleet in the country. If we had had any idea that you wanted to go to sea—"

Fran grinned. "You'd have thrown me in the hold and battened down the hatches."

Mother did not deny it. She said again, "You could be with your cousins."

The next spring when the *Sally* put into Plymouth a richly dressed young man with an air of quiet authority came aboard. "Master Tanner, I'm John Hawkins."

For once Adam Tanner looked impressed. "I've heard of you, Captain Hawkins. You and your brother, both."

"We're a little short of small vessels for coastwise trade," John said. "I've heard good reports of the master of the *Sally*. Think you could handle some cargoes for us? Be rather a steady thing."

"Sounds fine to me, Captain Hawkins!"

John glanced about the deck, saw Fran, and stared. "By all that's holy! Who's that lad?"

"Drake."

"Son of Edmund Drake?"

"Right."

"I knew it! I saw the resemblance!" He strode toward Fran, smiling, holding out his hand. "Welcome to Plymouth, lad! I'm your cousin. Don't suppose you remember me. You weren't more than four when you left Devon.

But I remember you very well! Master Tanner, could I take this lad ashore for the day to meet his relatives?"

"Of course, Captain Hawkins!"

Fran followed the velvet-clad back ashore. "Father wrote to you, didn't he?"

John looked startled, then smiled. "Clever lad."

"You weren't really surprised to see me."

"But it was better to do it that way," John said.

"Why?"

"We'll talk about that later." He took Fran to a shipyard to see a Hawkins ship a-building in the ways. "Like to be aboard her on her maiden voyage?"

"If it's after October of 'sixty-four. I'm prenticed till then."

"I think we can take care of that."

"No, we can't!" Fran blazed. "I gave a promise! I won't go back on my bargain!"

John smiled. "Steady, my young hothead. I think Master Tanner will be glad to release you. He'd rather have our good will than your services. If that suits him, you can't object, can you?"

"No, sir."

"Then get that scowl off your face, eh? We'll go see William. I don't suppose you remember him either, do you?"

"No, sir."

"He was very fond of you. Used to carry you around on his shoulder. You'll see more of William than of me here in Plymouth. I spend most of my time in London."

William's house was the finest place Fran had ever seen, with servants bowing and smiling. William was a heavy-set man who moved slowly and looked much older than John—until he smiled.

He shook hands, put his arm around Fran's shoulders, and said, "Welcome home, lad. I want you to feel at home here. Everything arranged, John?"

"Not yet, but it will be. Old Tanner practically rubbed his hands at the thought of Hawkins business."

When they returned to the *Sally* John smiled at Adam. "Master Tanner, I've been having an argument with this young hothead. I say his place is with his relatives. He refuses to ask for his release. In fact, if he had his way, I don't believe you'd even have had a chance to make your own decision about it."

Adam's eyebrows bristled. His eyes narrowed to slits. "So, Drake, you think a half-baked, ignorant prentice is worth more than the good will of the Hawkinses, eh?"

"I don't know!" Fran shouted. "But I do know that if I leave you it won't be because *I* broke *my* word!"

Adam's fist clenched slowly.

"Oh, come now, Master Tanner!" John said. "Don't be too hard on the lad. He doesn't realize what our business means to a coaster."

Adam wheeled to glare at John. "The devil with you and your business, both!"

"What?"

"I'll keep my prentice! I'll teach him more in a week than you'd teach him in a month! Because I know more than any half-dozen of your captains put together!"

For a moment John looked as dumfounded as Fran felt. Then he began to laugh. "Master Tanner, you and my young cousin are quite a pair! Keep your prentice! And you shall have Hawkins business, too. Here's my hand on it!" He shook hands with Adam, slapped Fran on the shoulder, and—still chuckling—left the *Sally*.

Adam looked after him with a puzzled frown, then wheeled to scowl at Fran. "Humph. Get this through your head, Drake. Don't think I'll be sparing you to spend the day with your fine-feathered cousins every time we put into Plymouth."

For once Adam's snarls didn't bother Fran. Hadn't Master Tanner risked losing Hawkins business to keep his prentice? Fran straightened and smiled. "No, sir! I understand, sir! My place is on the *Sally*. And I appreciate what I'm learning."

"Hah. Keep on, you'll be as smooth-tongued as your cousin. That one could talk his way out of hell. Come along. We'll see if you still know anything. Your day in Plymouth probably addled your brains."

In his cabin Adam began, "What's the weather side of a ship?"

He *must* think my brains are addled, Fran thought. I've known that since I was ten. But he answered, "The side the wind is striking."

"What's the lee side of a ship?"

Fran could feel his temper rising, but he answered, "The side away from the wind."

"What's a lee shore?"

"The shore that's protected from the wind!" Fran snapped.

Adam brightened. "Hah! Got you there! So a lee shore is protected from the wind? A lee shore, you fool, is the shore the wind is striking! The shore the wind will drive your ship on! A lee shore, you idiot, is the most dangerous thing in the world!"

Fran's ears burned. He stumbled, "I—I thought you said the lee of the land."

"But I didn't! Don't you know the difference yet between the lee of the land where you're protected from the wind—and a lee shore where you're at the mercy of the wind? Too bad! Because some day you'll drive on a lee shore and lose your ship! When she strikes and goes aground, and the wind pins her there, and the waves hammer her to pieces! Some day when you . . ."

Fran waited till the tirade ended, and said, "Yes, sir."

"If you were caught on a lee shore, with no anchorage, in a rising gale, what'd you do?"

Fran studied a moment. This was the hardest maneuver of all to remember. Slowly he began, "I'd haul up my mainsail and mizzen . . . have to haul both at the same time . . . shiver the main and mizzen topsails . . . put the helm hard alee . . . raise the foretack . . . let go the head bowlines . . . brace about the head yards sharp the other way . . ."

Adam stopped him with a snort. "Humph! That all the faster you'd give those orders? You'd be wrecked before you started! Why, you . . ."

Fran listened to another tirade and said "Yes, sir!" again.

Adam grilled him until darkness fell. He lighted a lantern and grilled him for another hour. He covered every harbor on the English Channel and on most of the North Sea. He covered the set of every stage of the tide. He covered every maneuver of handling a ship, fore-and-after, or square-rigger.

At last he said, "Humph. Well, I guess it's time for you to knuckle down to work. Get a little navigation in your head—if possible."

"What? But don't I—"

"You think you know navigation, Drake? Bah! Just pilotage. You can take your departure from one port, get your bearings, and set your course for another. Nothing to it—if you know about lee shores. But navigation—hah! What if you'd been at sea for weeks—maybe months—without sight of land? And you couldn't depend on your compass to give you true north? Then how'd you find your way?"

"I never thought of that."

"I've never seen any sign yet that you can think," Adam snarled. "You can memorize things and parrot them back.

In fact, you're the most amazing parrot I've ever known. Come along, Parrot, and I'll show you something."

They went on deck and stood in the darkness.

"Look at the sky."

Fran closed his eyes a moment, then looked. At first he saw only a few stars. Then by tens, hundreds, and thousands they began to prick the darkness with points of light.

"Before you're a navigator, Drake, that's what you have to know like the palm of your hand. The stars."

"All of them?"

"Don't be a fool. You have to know how to pick out the main stars from the mess. The moon and the stars by night, and the sun by day. You have to know when they'll be where. And then you have to know how to use them."

"Yes, sir. I see."

"I doubt it. Some day you may, if you can stand up to it. You might even learn to think."

Fran clenched his teeth and finally answered, "Yes, Master Tanner." Some day, he told himself, it will get easier.

But it never did. Day in, day out, Adam drove him harder. Drove his whole crew, for that matter. More and more often he stayed in his cabin and left the work to them.

Nothing seemed to bother Pedro, but in '61 Carey jumped ship.

"Don't blame him," Fran muttered. "When my prenticeship ends I hope I never see the *Sally* again!"

His prenticeship ended suddenly one night in '63. They were fighting a squall in the Channel when the *Sally* yawed wildly. Adam had slumped at the helm.

Fran grabbed it and fought to bring the ship under control. Pedro picked up the old man and carried him to his cabin. In a few moments he came back. "Master Tanner wants to see you."

Adam lay on his bunk with his eyes closed. "Drake?" he whispered. "Sit here by me. Not much time. Lots to say. Promise me this, Drake. Bury me at sea."

"Now, Master Tanner, you're not—"

"You know the answer to an order, Drake!" Even in a whisper Adam could snarl.

"Aye, aye, sir."

"I've driven you, lad." He clutched Fran's hand. "I've driven you. So little time. So much to learn. You understand?"

"Yes, sir."

"Wouldn't want you not to understand." He fumbled at a chain around his neck. "The key. Paper in my strongbox. Starboard end."

Fran found the paper—a single sheet, folded twice.

"Read it, Drake. Out loud."

It began, "I, Adam Tanner, considering the frailty of human nature, the many mishaps, accidents, and casualties . . ." It ended, "To Francis Drake, who has been like a beloved son, I leave all of which I die possessed, including the *Sally.*"

"Master Tanner, I—"

"I'll do the talking. Not much time. Courage, Drake! That's the thing. Your crew . . . waiting . . . always hardest. Waiting gnaws at a man's heart. Always remember, Drake . . ." After a while he slept.

Fran returned to the deck. "He thinks he's going to die."

"*Sí, señor.* For a long time he know it is coming. Stay with him."

That night and the next day Fran sat by the old man, listening whenever he wakened to talk.

The second night Adam's mind wandered. He seemed to be living again his days with the Portsmouth fleet. He sketched a salute. "God save the King!"

Fran gave the countersign. "Long to reign over us."

After a moment he covered the old man's face and went to tell Pedro.

"You want I get him ready to be buried at sea?" Pedro asked.

"You know how?"

"*Sí, señor.* You be at sea long as I have, you do it a hundred times."

"I'll take the helm."

"Aye, aye, sir. The course is full west, Master Drake."

Master Drake. For the first time it dawned on him. This

wonderful ship that answered his hand on the helm—she was his! *Master Drake! In command of his own ship!*

Odd, how the compass was blurring. . . . The rain had stopped and the sky was clear. . . .

When Pedro and Fran brought the *Sally* into Plymouth, Pedro said, "Here is a good place to sign on a crew, Master Drake."

"We could do with another man," Fran agreed.

"A whole new crew, sir. I think it be good if you have three men." Pedro smiled. "Me—I am going to jump ship."

"But, Pedro! You've always been with the *Sally!*"

"*Sí, señor*. Ever since you were a little boy."

"Oh . . . You don't want to sail under me for a master. Is that it?"

"*No, señor*. I think it be better you not have someone around to remember when you were a little boy. You be a man quicker."

"But what will I do without you?"

"You will command your ship, Master Drake! Now—maybe you go tell your cousins the *Sally* has a new master?"

Neither John nor William was in Plymouth, but Sedgely, one of their clerks, congratulated Fran on his good fortune. A crew for the *Sally?* He knew the very ones. He sent a boy dashing to find them.

"Those lads cut their teeth on a marlinspike," he said.

"The youngest one's still got things to learn, but he'll be the best of the lot some day."

The three lads came, shook hands, and called Fran "sir." Yes, they'd be proud to sail under a man who was trained by Adam Tanner. The youngest, Pip Newman, was not more than fourteen—a rangy, awkward pup of a lad, still all hands and feet. Though his hair was black he reminded Fran of Joe. He looked as full of mischief.

Fran swaggered down the street with the three of them, feeling ten feet tall.

Pedro was waiting on the *Sally*. He had his gear together. He talked to the lads a moment, then said, "*Adiós, señor.*"

"But—but—I want to talk to you." Fran led the way to his cabin. "Sit down, Pedro. There's so much—" He could think of nothing to say. "We—we've been through a lot, haven't we?"

"Yesterday is past, *señor*. This is the beginning of tomorrow. I say one thing. Then I go. You will be a better master than Adam Tanner."

"What? If I'm half the master he was I'll be—"

"You were born to be a happy man, *señor*. These years—they not kill it, I think. Try to remember, *señor*, how it feel once to be 'big brother.' Then you have a happy crew. They work like the devil for you." He held out his big hand. "*Adiós*. Go with God, my friend."

Fran said it in Spanish. "*Vaya con Dios, amigo.*"

He was glad to be busy for the next hour showing his crew over the *Sally* and answering their questions.

"You know what we think, sir?" Pip wore his ear-to-ear grin. "We think the *Sally* could use a bit of paint. We'd like to really shine her up for you!"

The *Sally's* next cargo was bound for Gravesend on the Thames. If only I could go to the Medway, Fran thought, and show . . . Then he laughed at himself. Why not? He was giving the orders now!

As they weighed anchor from Gravesend he said, "We'll stop one day on the Medway. My family is there."

"Aye, aye, sir!" The lads fell to swabbing the deck. The *Sally* was going to make eyes bug when she sailed into the Medway with her new master!

The sailors who remembered Fran pumped his hand, slapped him on the back, and cheered. They had always known he'd make good! No, they said, his family weren't on the *Clarissa* now. His father was vicar of Upchurch—not too far away. They gave him directions.

Fran took Pip ashore with him. "I want my brothers to see you. You make me think of Joe. We'll probably talk all night."

But Johnny and Joe were not there. They had gone to sea. Father sighed when he spoke of it. Mother said nothing, but her eyes seemed to accuse Fran of starting the whole thing.

Little Tommy was eight now. He shook hands, answered Fran's questions with "Yes, sir" and "No, sir" and soon edged out of the room.

The conversation dragged. Fran said he was glad things were going better. Father nodded. The silence lengthened. Mother and Pip had more to say. They talked of Devon.

After an hour Fran said he must get back to his ship. *Adam Tanner was right,* he thought. *Home life and seafaring don't mix.* But it would be different in Plymouth. Especially if his cousins were there. They'd know how he felt about the *Sally.*

William was away on a voyage, but John was in Plymouth, looking very thin, and brown as an Indian. "So," he said, "you're Master Drake."

"Yes, sir." Fran knew he was grinning like a fool. "We promise you careful handling of all cargo."

"If you want my advice—which you probably don't—you'll sell the *Sally.*"

"Why in the name of sense?"

John cocked an eyebrow. "Like the taste of command, eh? Glad you're done saying 'Aye, aye, sir'?"

"Anything wrong with that?"

"Not a thing, my young hothead, unless you let it stunt your growth. Tell me, do you still dream of 'commanding your own ship to far-off ports'?"

"Of course."

"And how will you get ready for that?" He smiled. "By

throwing out your chest and bossing three men on that little tub?"

"Don't call my ship a tub!" Fran yelled.

John put his arm around Fran's shoulders. "I know you like the sweet taste of command. But you need a few more years of 'Aye, aye, sir.' It's the only way you'll get ready for the future—for the big things I know you can do some day."

Fran jerked loose. "You *are* 'smooth-tongued,' aren't you? That's what Adam Tanner said. You could talk your way out of hell!" He strode out, slamming the door behind him.

4

"Women!"

How long he tramped the streets of Plymouth Fran did not know. Finally he went back to John Hawkins. "You're right. I'm ready to say 'Aye, aye, sir!' again. Soon as I can sell the *Sally.*"

"We can take care of that for you while you're gone," John said. "And, if you like, I'll invest what you have. My last voyage earned forty per cent for her shareholders."

Fran whistled. "Where was that?"

"To the West Indies. Trading with the Spanish colonies."

"But I thought the King of Spain—"

John smiled. "Owns half the world? And the King of Portugal the other half? You know how that notion got started?"

"No, sir."

"Because one of the Popes—Alexander the Sixth—decided to divide the world between them. But who said it was his to divide? You know what the King of France said to the King of Spain about it? 'Your Majesty and the King of Portugal have divided the world between you, leaving no part of it to me. Show me, I pray you, the will of our father, Adam, so that I may know he has truly made you his only universal heirs.' That's what France—and the rest of the world—thought of the idea. It's idiotic. So—I'm trading with the Spanish colonies. The West Indies are very far from Spain. And the colonials know a bargain when they see it. I'll invest your money for you, unless you're afraid of the risk."

"Don't call me a coward!"

"A hothead, yes. A coward, no. That's the last thing I'd ever call you. One of our ships, the *Provider*, sails tomorrow for the Canaries. She's short one hand in the fo'c'sle."

The fo'c'sle! At last Fran mustered a smile. "Aye, aye, sir."

"Not going to be easy, is it?"

"You didn't intend for it to be, did you?"

"While you're still Master Drake, commander of the *Sally*, you have one thing to do that will be harder."

"I don't believe it."

"Explain things to your crew. A master never dodges something just because it's hard to say."

"You're right. It will be harder. . . . Might as well get it over with."

His crew listened in shocked silence. "The next master of the *Sally*," Fran promised, "will have my recommendation of you three in writing. That you're the best crew that ever sailed out of Plymouth."

"But, sir!" Pip said. "It won't be any fun without you!"

"We'll be in the same boat there," Fran told him. "I'll not be having much fun, either."

During the next three years Fran saw very little of his cousins. Sometimes, when Fran came into Plymouth, Sedgely gave him a note from one of them. The first note was from John:

> *So you had a taste of the cat-o'-nine-tails. Regrettable. You'll have to learn to curb your temper. A man who is not master of himself can never be a master of others.*

A few months later there was a note from William:

> *I was pleased to hear that you were promoted to purser, and handled all the ship's accounts without a single mistake. Congratulations. I'm proud of you.*
>
> *One other thing I heard pleased me even more—that when you were promoted, the men before the mast cheered for you. The man who wins the affection and respect of that mob is well on his way to successful command!*

The summer of '67 there was another note from John:

> *When you return I'll probably be in London, making final arrangements for my next voyage to the West Indies. I'll be taking two of the Queen's ships—the* Jesus of Lubeck *and the* Minion, *and*

four of my own—the William and John, *the* Angel, *the* Swallow, *and the* Judith.

I should like you to go as captain of the Judith. *Sign on a crew of twenty-five, and provision her for four months. Get ready as fast as possible.*

But, before you lade your cargo, have a ship's carpenter check the ship thoroughly *and make any necessary repairs. I suggest Tom Moone. He's one of the best.*

Captain Drake! In command of his own ship! Sailing to far-off ports! Fran swaggered up the streets of Plymouth to find Tom Moone.

Tom was as big and good-natured as Pedro had been. There the resemblance ended. Tom's sandy thatch was sprinkled with gray. Nothing could excite him or hurry him. While Fran walked the deck and fought down his impatience Tom prowled over the *Judith,* scraping at paint, jabbing at timbers.

At last he said, "Sound as an oak, sir."

Fran exploded. "Thank heaven you're satisfied!"

Tom only blinked and grinned. "Signed on your crew yet, sir?"

"Haven't even started."

"May I be the first man you sign on?"

"You? But, Tom, you could have a berth on the bigger ships—the flagship, even! You could—"

"Maybe I'm lazy. Be less work to do on the *Judith.* Maybe I'm curious. I heard three Devon lads say it was 'fun' to sail with you. Crazy thing to say about a master. How about it, sir?"

Fran held out his hand. "I just hope the rest of my crew can measure up to you."

"Ain't going to be easy to find men, sir. The other three Hawkins ships already have their crews and are taking in supplies. For the Queen's ships Captain Hawkins can press men, and make them serve. Where you'll find a crew in a hurry—"

From the water a shout reached them. "Ahoy, the *Judith!*"

A boatload of Devon lads approached. Pip Newman, grinning from ear to ear, was waving. "Heard about you and the *Judith,* Captain Drake! We want to sign on!"

A dozen boys swarmed aboard with him.

Tom looked them over and nodded. Fran signed them on.

"And I'll have thirty more for you tomorrow!" Pip promised.

"The *Judith* will carry only twenty-five," Fran said. "She's just fifty tons."

Pip grinned. "Glad we got here first! We'll fill up the crew tomorrow!"

They shook hands all around, promised to be back on the double with their gear, and returned to their boat. They pulled for the shore, shouting a chanty.

"Pip's quite a boy," Tom said. "Born leader."

"He know enough to be my master?" Fran asked.

"You couldn't do better, sir." For a moment Tom watched the boat. "Likely lads. Wonder how many we'll bring home again?"

"They lose a lot of men on these expeditions?"

"No more than average, I guess. But any voyage that long—ten months or so—well, a captain never gets back with all of them, does he?" Tom shook his head. "Every time I anchor in Plymouth my old woman asks, 'How many came back?' Sticks in a man's craw. I never can think of an answer for my old woman."

"Your wife?" Fran asked.

"No, sir! Bad enough trying to explain things to your mother, without taking on a wife!"

"You sound like Adam Tanner. 'Women! Don't ever get married, Drake! Home life and seafaring don't mix!' "

Tom nodded. "He was right. Women . . ."

Fran smiled and hurried ashore to see about supplies. He must have the *Judith* ready to weigh anchor when the Queen's ships arrived in Plymouth Harbor.

By dint of day-and-night work he got ready. Then waited . . . and waited. No sign of the Queen's ships. No word from London.

John Hawkins turned up without the ships. He came to Fran's cabin and said just one word as he entered. "Women!"

"What's wrong?"

"I'm a loyal subject of Her Majesty!" John declared. "I've never said a word against her. Never expect to. But

—*if I did*—I'd say she has a weathercock for a mind!"

"What's the trouble?"

"Oh, some political standing-off-and-on with Spain!" Then a reluctant smile chased his frown. "I'll say this for the Queen. England is about five hundred per cent better off than when she came to the throne in 'fifty-eight. I didn't think she'd last six months. It's been almost eight years. She's certainly kept the rest of Europe wondering what she'd do next!"

"And her own countrymen, too?" Fran asked.

John sighed and nodded.

"The expedition to the West Indies is forbidden?"

"Oh, nothing that simple!" John said. "We're to stand by for further orders! When she makes up her mind she'll send the *Jesus* and the *Minion* around to Plymouth—maybe. The *Judith* ready to sail?"

"Yes, confound it! I've been working my crew like—"

"Then you may stand by, too. Good experience for a captain. And who knows? Some day you might command a naval vessel. If you ever do the ability to stand by and wait will be priceless!"

"I know what would bring our orders in a hurry, sir," Pip suggested one day to John Hawkins. "If Captain Drake and I went out in the country to see my people. We wouldn't more than get there till you'd be sending a rider posthaste after us."

"Not a bad idea." John smiled at Fran. "Go tramp

around the country a few days—before you walk a hole through the deck of the *Judith.*"

Pip hired two horses. "You've ridden, haven't you, Captain Drake?"

"Not much, but I know you don't mount from starboard."

"Just walk around a lot when we get there," Pip said, "and you'll be all right."

They ambled through the countryside and finally stopped on the rise of a hill. Pip pointed to a thatched roof in the midst of flowers. "That's it! Uh—one thing, Captain Drake. My mother and sister—of course my sister may be married and gone—but we won't tell them you're a mariner. They—"

"I know," Fran said. "Women! Tell them I'm thinking of buying a farm if you want to!"

Pip pulled a long face. "Oh, I couldn't do that, sir. I wasn't brought up to lie." His eyes danced.

I wonder how he will introduce me? Fran thought.

When they stopped in front of the cottage a slim girl with short brown curls came racing to meet them, calling, "Mother! Mother! It's Pip!"

The door opened and Pip's mother hurried down the path, her round face beaming.

Pip lifted them both off their feet in bear hugs, then, with an arm around each of them, winked at Fran over their heads, and introduced him as "Mr. Drake." He said, "I don't know what will interest Mr. Drake most. Maybe to look at farms. His family came from around here. Maybe he'd like to settle here himself, some day."

Mary's blue eyes sparkled. "That's wonderful, Mr. Drake. I'll show you around! I know which farms could be bought."

"Uh—uh—" Pip floundered, "you'd better not tell anyone he's buying a farm."

"Of course not," Mary promised. "We won't say he's looking at farms. He'll just be—you know—*looking.*"

Pip tousled her curls. "She always talks that way. Guess it makes sense to her. You have any idea what she means, Mr. Drake?"

"Oh, yes," Fran said. "I had a younger brother who talked exactly that way—when he was six."

Mary laughed with them and reached her hand. "Come along, Mr. Drake."

All that afternoon the two roamed the countryside, and Mary talked of the farms. From somewhere in the past memories nudged at Fran's mind.

"I thought I had forgotten everything," he said, "but it halfway comes back to me."

"Of course," Mary said. "Nobody could really forget Devon." For a time she was silent. Then, dreamily, as though talking to herself, she said, "A thatched cottage, smothered in flowers. The waking-up sounds in the morning. The sleepy sounds at night. Evening was the sweet time. The pot bubbling on the fire. Everything waiting for Father. Then supper. The children in a row at the table, clutching their spoons, waiting for prayers to be over. Maybe they squirmed a little bit when the prayer was long."

"I was four," Fran said, "and Johnny was two, and little Joe was just a— You're amazing! That's exactly the way it was!"

"Nothing amazing about it, Mr. Drake. How else could you remember Devon?"

That night Fran told Pip, "This joke has gone far enough. You've got to tell Mary I'm not here to look at farms."

"But everything's so peaceful! Nobody picking on me about being a sailor. Aren't you having a good time?"

"Of course I am. Mary's a wonderful girl. She's the—the—I'm having a fine time."

"Then why spoil it all?"

"When she finds out I'm Captain Drake—"

"Not much chance of that. They never know what's going on in Plymouth. When we get back from this voyage we'll come out again and tell them. Mother'll laugh at the joke."

"Mary won't. She'll remember all the trouble she went to, showing me farms, and—"

"Oh, she'll probably be married and gone," Pip said. "So there's nothing to worry about, is there?"

For a moment Fran was silent, trying to digest the thought that struck him. *I don't want her to be married and gone!* He said, "You've got to tell her the truth. If you don't, I will."

The next night Pip asked, "How'd she take it?"

"I didn't get around to it," Fran said, "but tomorrow . . ."

Instead, the next day he found himself saying, "I don't know much about girls. I never had a sister. Tell me—what kind of husband does a girl dream about?"

Mary's laughter bubbled. "You don't know much about them, do you? It would depend on the girl."

"What about you?"

She stared thoughtfully up at a tree. "A man I could be happy with. We'd laugh at the same things and love the same things. He'd be a farmer, of course."

"You'd never marry a sailor?"

"Never."

I'd feel better if she hadn't said it so quietly, Fran thought. "Not even if you fell in love with him?"

"But I wouldn't." She said that quietly, too. "I'd be just as apt to fall in love with a man on his way to the gallows."

"Oh, come now! All sailors aren't criminals."

"They're condemned men. On their way to die. Sooner or later the most of them are lost at sea." She shivered. "Please, don't let's talk about sailors! I'm glad you're a friend of Pip's. He admires you so much. If anybody could turn him from the sea—"

Behind them they heard a halloo. Pip, riding one horse and leading the other, came pounding toward them. "Captain Drake! Captain Drake! A messenger from Plymouth! We're to report to our ship immediately!"

"Oh . . ." That was all Mary said.

"Mary, I was trying to tell you, but—"

There was no time to say more. Pip was beside them, bending down to tell his sister good-by.

Mary kissed him and shook hands with Fran. "Good-by, Captain Drake. I'm glad you had so much fun." She wheeled and walked away.

"Took it all right, didn't she?" Pip said cheerfully.

"Oh, yes! Glad I had so much fun!"

Pip was too excited to notice anything. "Good for Mary. You know, she's all right—for a sister. Some women—"

"Yes, women!" Fran flung himself into the saddle and urged his horse to a gallop.

He spent the ride planning a letter to Mary. By the time they reached Plymouth he knew exactly what he would say. He would begin "My very dear Mary." As for what would come next his mind was still a blank.

5

Wanted–a letter of marque

Before they sailed Fran managed to write his letter and send it to Mary:

My very dear Mary

I have nothing to say now that you would want to listen to. I can't blame you. But when I get home I'm coming out to see you. The minute we're back I shall hire the fastest horse in Plymouth. Maybe I'll hire two and ride them in relays.

Look for me by August—or by September at the latest.

Your loving and obedient servant
F. Drake

The next September the fleet was more than four thousand miles from home, fighting to survive a hurricane in the Gulf of Mexico. When the storm passed and the ships got together again the *William and John* was missing and the *Jesus of Lubeck* was barely afloat.

They could not start home, Captain Hawkins said, until they had repaired the *Jesus*. She was leaking so badly there were fish swimming around in her bilge.

Back across the Gulf of Mexico they limped toward the only possible refuge—San Juan de Ulloa, the harbor of Veracruz. Not much of a refuge. No protection but a single low island, little more than a sandspit, lying off the coast.

As they neared the harbor a Spanish boat challenged them. Who were they, and what were they doing in these waters?

John Hawkins was calmly courteous. "Ships of Her Majesty, the Queen of England. We are on a peaceful mission. All we want is to anchor long enough to trim our ships. We shall pay for everything we need. Liberally. With gold."

The Spanish put their heads together. At last they gave permission. Not much of an anchorage, they said. They would have to secure their headfasts to the chains on the island, and put out sternfasts to the moorings in the water. The Spanish returned to the mainland.

There was a flurry of protests when the English removed eleven big guns from the *Jesus* and set them up on the island.

Again John Hawkins was calmly courteous. He had to get weight out of the flagship to make repairs.

The Spanish shrugged and left them again.

John Hawkins sent powder and shot after the guns, and

detailed men to stand by them night and day. "I hope," he told his captains, "we'll have no trouble. But it's just about time for the *flota*—the treasure fleet—to arrive from Spain. When they come to take home the treasure from the mines of Mexico they are well armed. I have promised to keep the peace with Spain. I intend to. But" —and he looked toward the guns—"I prefer to argue from a position of strength."

The next morning when the captains were on the *Jesus,* planning the work that must be done, a flourish of trumpets and ruffle of drums called every man on deck. There, bearing down on the harbor, was the *flota*—thirteen ships —all bigger than the *Jesus.*

John Hawkins summoned a boat and went to the flagship of the *flota.* His captains looked at one another and shook their heads. It was one thing to deal with the colonials, and something else again to defy the haughty officers from the homeland!

"Someone said once," Fran remarked, "that he could 'talk his way out of hell.' I hope he was right."

Evidently Adam Tanner was. John returned to the *Jesus* as calm as usual. "We've come to terms. We'll allow the *flota* to anchor. They'll allow us to hold the island long enough to make repairs. No Spaniards will come to the island unless they leave their weapons behind."

"How did the haughty *dons* like that?" Fran asked.

"Not too well," John admitted. "But they agreed. After all, we do have the upper hand. We have fire power enough to keep them out of the harbor. If a gale rose from the north it would drive them on a lee shore." He smiled briefly. "So I was arguing from a position of strength."

All that day the crews of the *flota* were busy warping their ships into the harbor. Then Spaniards—without their weapons—swarmed over the island to talk in smiles and gestures with the English gun crews. For the next few days the English worked on the *Jesus* and the Spaniards came and went on the island.

Pip returned to the *Judith* one day humming a Spanish tune. "You know, I wish I could talk to them. Get acquainted. They're good fellows, really."

Fran studied the crowds around the gun crews with narrowed eyes. More Spaniards than usual this afternoon. Was something in the wind? Or were they merely there to stretch their legs?

He could not see the Spanish ships from the *Judith*. She was anchored farthest from the Spanish fleet. Perhaps if he took a stroll up the island . . . He climbed out on the bowsprit and dropped to the sand.

He had not taken five steps when a trumpet blared. At the signal the Spaniards around the gun crews moved as one man. Each slid a dagger from his sleeve and stabbed the nearest Englishman. Guns boomed. A tangle of broken masts and rigging crashed on the deck of the *Jesus*.

Fran leaped, grabbed a hawser and started to climb

aboard the *Judith*. Four knives whistled by his head and buried their points in the hull of his ship.

He reached the deck roaring orders. "Cut the headfasts! Haul on the sternfasts!" In the bedlam of battle he worked the *Judith* clear and around the east end of the island. Then he came about and stood in for orders.

The *Jesus* would never sail again, but she was making her last minutes count as a bulwark for the *Minion*. The odds, though, were hopeless. The *Angel* was sinking, and the *Swallow* disabled.

Fran got his orders, darted in, went alongside the *Minion*, and took all the men and supplies the *Judith* could handle.

"Get outside with her!" John Hawkins yelled from the *Jesus*. "I'll make it with the *Minion!*"

Under his cool command the men were working as smoothly as though they were at a dockside in England. Part of them were blasting away with the larboard guns of the *Jesus;* others were moving stores to the *Minion*.

Then two Spanish ships began to burn as they drifted toward the *Jesus*. Fireships! The crew on the *Minion* panicked, cut their cables and got under way. If John Hawkins had not leaped, they'd have left him on the *Jesus*.

Through a hail of shot the *Judith* and the *Minion* escaped and anchored beyond Spanish guns. Dozens of wounded men crowded the deck of the *Judith*.

"I'll see what the score is, sir." Tom Moone went forward and worked his way back, making a quick check. "Forty in bad shape," he reported. "Five amputations to do. Eight dead. Some more ain't going to pull through. We've got our work cut out this night. Wonder how many can stand to help with the amputations?"

Then a dreaded norther broke over them, threatening to drive them on the lee shore. No time to think of the wounded until they had beaten their way to the safety of open water. They must wait on the pitching deck, exposed to the lashing rain.

The sky had paled to a before-dawn gray when Fran bent over the last man, sprawled face down. Dead. He knew that before he touched him. It was Pip.

"They'll pay for this!" he whispered. "*And the price is going to be high!*"

At dawn the *Judith* was alone on the storm-tossed water. No sign of the *Minion.* Had she gone aground and broken up? Or had she clawed her way off the lee shore and reached open water? Was she standing by, searching for him? Or making her way east across the gulf? If she were still afloat but in distress she might fire a gun to . . . No, Fran realized, they could not fire signal guns now. That would betray their whereabouts to the Spanish.

For two days he circled, searching for the *Minion.* No sign of her. The second night he had to face his situation. Fifty men on the *Judith.* Too many for her supplies. Even with rationing their food would not last more than two weeks. Not nearly long enough for the journey home—

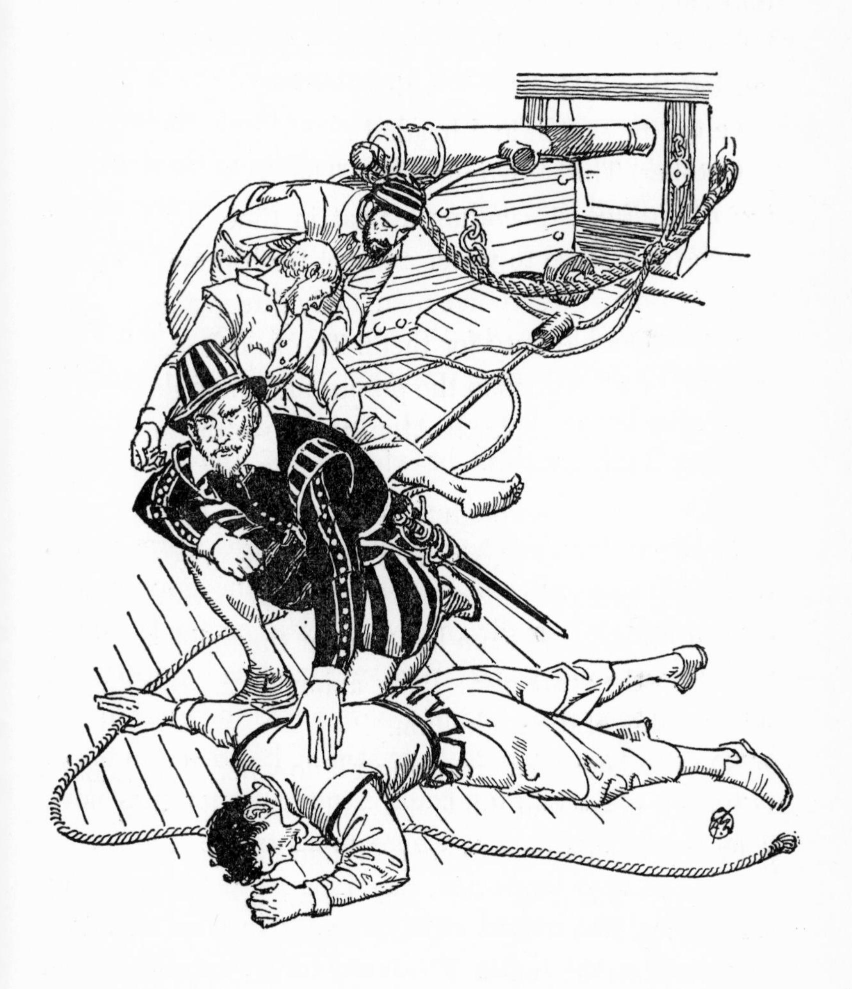

east for one thousand miles across the gulf, then through the Florida Straits and more than four thousand miles north and east back to Plymouth. He knew that every day he delayed starting home would lessen his chances of getting there. Heartsick with grief and baffled fury he gave up the search and headed east.

October. Thirty-two men left. The *Judith* crawled up the Florida coast, sending a boat in time and again to search for a place to water and get fresh provisions.

November. Twenty-five men. Only fifteen able to work the ship. Double duty for them. The *Judith* was leaking badly. They had to man the pumps night and day.

December. The North Atlantic. A storm bore down from the northwest.

Tom staggered through the sleet to shout in Fran's ear. "We've got a mutiny, sir. The men have given up. Just laid down to die."

"*But they can't!*" Fran left Tom at the helm and went to talk to the scarecrows lying about in the fo'c'sle. He said nothing of their rebellion.

"Do you know the first thing I'll do when I get back?"

"What makes you think you will?" one muttered.

Fran pretended not to hear. "I'll go to London and ask for a letter of marque. You know about letters of marque?"

They did not answer.

"A letter of marque is the government's permission to prey on the shipping of an enemy. And that's what I'm going to do! I'll raid the Caribbean from the Spanish Main to the Straits of Yucatán! I'll . . ."

How long he talked, and what he said, he could not remember. Finally two men struggled to their feet and staggered through the door.

Cold as it was Fran wiped sweat from his face. *"Courage, Drake! . . . Pouring courage into your men—sometimes it's like pouring water down a rat hole."*

Well, he'd roused them for a moment. If they reached Plymouth by Christmas their courage might last. If not . . .

On January 20 the *Judith* anchored in Plymouth with fifteen men.

Two boats sped over the water to meet them. Three of the men in the first boat were from the crew of the *William and John.* They looked very fit and well fed.

"What the devil happened to you?" Fran yelled.

"We thought all the rest of the fleet was lost in the hurricane, sir," one said. "So we came home. You see—"

Fran cut him off and asked about the *Minion.* No, no sign of her. They said they were sorry, mighty sorry, and began to lower the sick men over the side.

The second boat brought William Hawkins. He took one look about him and said, "We'll talk later. After every man of you is ashore and cared for, with some warm food in his belly."

It seemed to Fran that all Plymouth was in the streets —five women for every man. Women pleading for news of their men, blocking his way, grabbing at his sleeves, begging, weeping.

"Please let us through," William said over and over. "Please let us through. Can't you see Captain Drake is dead on his feet?"

" '*How many came back?' Sticks in a man's craw. I never can think of any answer for my old woman.*"

As Fran told William of San Juan de Ulloa his cousin seemed to age before his eyes.

"So it looks as though the *Judith* is the only ship that escaped?" William asked. "And you brought home fifteen men." He gripped the arms of his chair. "If I write a request for a letter of marque how soon will you feel like riding to London?"

"As soon as I can saddle a horse!"

"No use starting at night. The roads aren't safe after dark. Get some rest."

"I've a letter to write, myself."

He told Mary of the Spanish treachery and of Pip's death.

> *. . . I know I can't say anything to ease your sorrow. Only that I grieve with you. I loved Pip as I love my own brothers.*
>
> *I think you know I love you. I hoped when I came back I could buy you a farm. That I could make you believe I could love a farm and the sea, too. But I lost everything I had.*
>
> *I must go to London immediately. When I get*

back I'd like to come to see you. A letter in care of my cousin, William Hawkins of Plymouth, would reach me.

If only he could talk to her—could tell her all the dreams he had for the two of them! But what was the use now? He signed it, "Your loving and obedient servant, F. Drake." He flung himself down, boots and all, and slept.

He dreamed of her. In his dream he had come back, triumphant, the *Judith* decorated with flags and streamers. He and Mary were standing in a church. The minister was saying, "Do you, Mary, take this man . . ." when William shook him.

"Sorry to wake you, but it's dawn."

"I'm sorry, too," Fran said. "In another half minute . . ." He shrugged. That was all over. He gave William the letter for Mary. "You'll see that it's delivered? And if there's an answer you'll save it for me?"

"Indeed I will. She means a lot to you, Fran?"

"More than I'll ever mean to her, I'm afraid."

"You could ride out to see her now. A day more or less wouldn't matter about starting for London."

"I'm not doing anything till I get that letter of marque! Is your request ready?"

"Yes. I've worded it as strongly as I know how. I hope it's effective."

"If anything else needs saying," Fran promised, "I can say it! They'll listen to me!"

But William Cecil of the Queen's council pursed his lips and shook his head. They'd have to give the matter very careful consideration. Letters of marque were not issued unless countries were at war.

"What do you call the action at San Juan de Ulloa?" Fran asked.

Regrettable, Cecil admitted. But no war had been declared. England was at peace. And she must have peace. She would gain more by one year of peace than by ten years of war. He stood. No need, he said, to detain Captain Drake longer. They would send word to William Hawkins in Plymouth.

Fran stormed back to Plymouth, riding each horse to a lather and changing it for a fresh one. He was with William Hawkins when a servant knocked and entered, breathless. News of the *Minion!* She was standing off Plymouth Sound. She needed a fresh crew. The few survivors couldn't bring her into the harbor.

Fran was in the first boat that raced to the aid of the *Minion,* and the first man on board. He hurried to John's cabin, knocked and entered. "John! Thank God you—"

John Hawkins, skeleton thin, with haunted eyes, glared at him. "What the devil happened to you?"

"I don't understand?"

"There I was with the *Minion* hopelessly overcrowded and short of supplies. Two hundred men and not enough food for two weeks! And you—"

Fran clenched his fists till his fingernails bit into the

palms. "Sir, I was more overloaded for the size of my ship, and shorter of supplies, than you. After the storm I searched for two days, and—"

"And then turned tail and ran for home!" John slammed out of the cabin.

Fran sat in a daze. He was dimly aware that the ship was in motion, that it stopped again, that men were going ashore.

At last he went on deck.

A sailor saluted. "Captain Hawkins' compliments, sir. A boat is waiting to take you ashore, sir."

Something in the man's voice caused Fran to look at him. It was one of the crew of the *William and John*—one of the men Fran had yelled at, "What the devil happened to you?"

6

Demoted

On shore, Fran hesitated, then set his jaw and went back to William's house. John was not there. He had started immediately for London, William said.

"He's heartbroken over what happened to his men, Fran. Did he tell you about it?"

Fran shook his head and slumped in a chair.

"After two weeks they were so short of food that half the men begged to be put ashore. They preferred to take their chances with the natives or the Spaniards. So one hundred men from the *Minion* are in Spanish territory. Heaven knows what will happen to them. John's a sick man—a sick man."

Fran didn't know whether William was apologizing for John's accusations or merely stating a fact. He didn't ask.

"We can't make any plans," William said, "until we hear from him."

And when we do hear, Fran thought, his plans won't include me. "*So you turned tail and ran for home!*" He wondered if he'd ever forget the sting of those words.

"Perhaps you'd like to go see Mary Newman?" William suggested. No, he admitted, no answer had come to Fran's letter, but—

"It's no use then," Fran said.

"Anything else you'd like to do?"

"Yes. The first time you've a ship bound for the Medway I'd like to go see my people. It's been a long time. I've written to them. I don't know if they ever got my letters. I've never heard. Right now I'd like to . . ." He stopped. *I'd like to feel that I belong to somebody.* "I'd like to see them," he said.

"But Fran, hadn't you . . . No, you've had no chance to hear. Your father is dead. And his will mentioned no one but Thomas. He was the youngest boy, wasn't he? So the rest of the family is dead or—unaccounted for."

"Johnny and Joe?"

"They went to sea, didn't they? Probably lost. A good many men are."

Fran stared unseeing into the fire, trying to fight the tide of desolation that swept over him.

"Feel ready for a turn at sea?" William asked.

Fran looked up hopefully. Maybe he wasn't going to be banished from Hawkins ships after all. Maybe—

"One of the Queen's ships is in port just now," William said. "The *Gloria.* She's on duty patrolling the Channel. They are short a gunner's mate."

No—it wasn't to be duty on a Hawkins ship. Ex-Captain Drake could be a gunner's mate at six shillings a month. Fran got up. "Will they accept a man named Francis Drake, or should I call myself something else?"

"I've recommended my cousin, Francis Drake, to them," William said quietly, "to serve a three-months' term of duty."

"I'm sorry. And thank you, sir." Fran started out, then turned. "If a letter—"

"I'll see that you get it," William promised. "Fast pinnaces are always in touch with the ships on patrol. They're very handy little vessels."

"Yes." And Fran's bitterness came back. "Make me think of the *Sally*. Who knows? If I work hard I might get to command one of them some day." Then he flushed, and said again, "I'm sorry." He saluted. "I'll report to the *Gloria*, sir."

Mr. Henderson, the master gunner of the *Gloria*, was a hard-bitten old fellow with a temper to match Adam Tanner's. Fran stood silent under the whiplash of his tongue and said "Aye, aye, sir!" to his orders.

After a month the old man unbent enough to ask, "You married, Drake?"

"No, sir."

"Any family?"

"One brother. But he wouldn't remember me."

"No one you love?"

Fran dodged the answer. "Not a single, solitary soul in

the world cares whether I'm alive or dead."

"We're in the same boat." Mr. Henderson actually smiled. "The Queen would approve of us, Drake. She's alone, too."

"Alone? With her court, her—"

"Humph. Dozens of people all smiling and bowing. Some with knives up their sleeves. How'd you feel, Drake, if you had to live that way? What if you knew some shipmate was plotting to knife you, but you didn't know which one? That's her life. Alone—with an impossible job—and mighty few men she can depend on to help her."

"When she's ready for a little action," Fran said, "I'll volunteer."

Henderson snorted. "Wait for that time and you'll grow a gray beard. She doesn't dare fight. She can't afford a war. She doesn't have any treasure fleets pouring gold into her coffers like Philip of Spain. You have any idea how much he spends to keep the Low Countries under his thumb? I've seen his ships plowing the Channel with supplies for his armies in the Netherlands. He spends enough on that fight in a month to run England for a year. Forget about war, Drake. Just hope we can keep the peace."

"Like we did at San Juan de Ulloa?" Fran asked. "The next time I'm in the Caribbean—"

"You and what fleet of what ships?"

A pinnace hailed the *Gloria* and sent dispatches aboard. An officer riffled through the letters and glanced up. "We have anyone named Drake?"

Fran's heart hammered in his throat. "Right here, sir."

The letter was from William. No word yet, he said, from anybody.

When Fran returned to Plymouth after his three months' duty the news was the same. No word from Mary, William said. No letter of marque.

"Then give me one ship—just a small one—and provisions for two months. Just enough to get me to the Caribbean! I promise you, with God's help, I'll bring that ship back and make Philip pay for the voyage!"

"Do you know how many Spanish ships ply the Caribbean from port to port?"

Fran shrugged. "Fifty, perhaps. Maybe a hundred."

"There are more than two hundred," William told him.

Fran shrugged again. "All the better. I'm going to depend on them for supplies."

"And at least half of them are bigger than the *Judith*. If they boarded your ship they could—"

"They'd have to catch me first. Give me a handy, weatherly little vessel, and I can outsail anything afloat."

William's eyes twinkled. "Mighty sure of yourself, aren't you? But, you know, I've half a notion you could do it." Then he frowned. "There's one problem, Fran. The hundred men who went ashore from the *Minion*. They may be in Spanish hands. If they are, the first Spaniard you killed could mean the death of every one of them. By slow torture."

"I'm not going over there to kill Spaniards. I want to

do something that will really bother Philip of Spain. I'll prick him where it'll hurt. Make him bleed gold. That's the way to make him suffer."

William rubbed his chin. "Hmmm. Suppose you give me a few days to think about it. Meantime, there's something I want you to do."

"Yes, sir!"

"Ride out to see Mary Newman. Maybe she did answer your letter. Letters can go astray, you know."

"Is that supposed to give me hope?"

"At least it gives you an excuse for going, doesn't it? I've a little cottage here in Plymouth you could have."

"I couldn't pay rent on a market stall."

"I could wait for the rent. Take it out of those profits you'll make in the Caribbean."

"You're mighty sure she'll have me, aren't you?"

"No, Fran. I just believe you ought to settle it, one way or the other."

"Yes. No use to keep wondering. All right. I'll go."

Once more Fran reined in his horse on the rise of a hill and looked down on a thatched roof among flowers. He thought of the sparkle in Mary's eyes that first day, of the way Pip teased her. . . . *Pip!*

Slowly, as a man going to his doom, he rode on, dismounted before the cottage, and tied his horse. More slowly he walked to the door. As he lifted his hand to knock the door opened. Mary looked at him, tried to speak, then buried her face in her hands, sobbing.

He put his arms around her. "There, there!" All the things he had planned to say left him. "There, there!" He gave her his handkerchief.

"Thank you." She dabbed at her eyes. "I didn't mean to do that."

"Did you get my letter?"

She nodded. "And Tom Moone came to see me. And some of the other men."

"I wondered if you got the letter. I didn't get any answer."

"I tried to answer it. But I just couldn't. Let's walk. I don't want Mother to see me all weepy."

They walked down the lane in silence. The longer the silence the harder Fran hunted for words.

Mary spoke first. "Captain Drake?"

"Yes, Mary?"

"I don't blame you about Pip."

"Thank you." Again the silence. "Confound it, Mary. I had so many things I was going to say!"

"Tell me about when you were a little boy. The other time I did all the talking. About farms."

He told her of the *Clarissa* and his years under Adam Tanner.

"You've never known anything but the sea," Mary said. "And you'll never give up the sea, will you, Captain Drake?"

"Not if the sea will have me." He told her of John Hawkins' accusations.

Mary's eyes blazed. "Why that—that *dog!* He ought to be hanged!"

For the first time in months the cold lump in Fran's chest didn't feel so heavy. "Now, now! You don't know what he'd gone through."

"I know what you'd gone through! Because Tom Moone told me! If I hadn't loved you before, I'd have—" She stopped.

"Mary!"

Her next words were muffled against his coat. "I didn't mean to fall in love with a sailor. I knew what my life would be. A little while together now and then. Most of the time waiting and wondering and hoping and praying. And waking up in the night scared to death and—" She shuddered.

"I can't get you the farm I wanted to buy for you. There's a cottage in Plymouth we may have, but—"

"Maybe Plymouth's the place for a sailor's wife. I'll be with a lot of women feeling the same way."

"There will be one difference," he said. "I won't be sailing on trading expeditions. I'll be sailing against Philip of Spain."

She caught her breath, then said hopefully, "Maybe you won't get your letter of marque."

"With a letter of marque or without it!"

"Oh, no! If you did that you'd be a pirate!"

"I'll never fight as a pirate. He attacks any ship of any country, guts her of treasure, sends her to the bottom, and lets her crew die. I'll never kill an unarmed man. But the Caribbean from the Spanish Main to the Straits of Yucatán will remember my name!"

She paled and stared at him, wordless.

"I love you, Mary. But I want you to know what you're doing. If you say 'yes' to me, you'll be marrying a man who is at war with the King of Spain."

"Yes, Captain Drake."

He smiled. "My mother called me 'Fran.' "

It was as Mary had said it would be. A little while together, then a night when Tom Moone knocked on the door of their cottage. "All ready, sir! And a fine, thick fog to sail in!"

"It's the Caribbean, isn't it?" Mary said.

"Let's say 'destination unknown.' Then, if anyone asks questions, you can say you don't know." Fran smiled at her.

"I can say, 'He did not tell me where he was going.' But I know. I can always tell when you dream of the Caribbean. You call out, 'Beat to quarters!' I cannot hear your drum, but I know it's beating." She stood very straight. "God be with you."

"Now there's a proper wife for a sailing man!" Tom Moone picked up Fran's gear and held the door open for him.

Fran went out into the misty night. He paused by the window to look back. Mary was standing where he had left her. Not so straight now. Her face was buried in her hands.

When his ship had cleared the Channel Fran talked to his crew. "Of all the men who volunteered to sail with me I chose you. All were lads of Devon—the handiest mariners in the world. I chose you for something else. Because I knew you could keep your tongues between your teeth. Promise me this: Never, as God is your witness, will you tell anybody anything about this voyage—where we go—what we see—what we do."

They raised their right hands and promised.

Months later, when their ship, homeward bound, paused off the coast of England, again the drums called all hands on deck.

Fran looked at their sunburned faces. "Well, we can't claim we spent our time hunting for the Northwest Passage, can we?" He laughed with them, then sobered. "But —where we were—what we did—no man must say."

"Not a word, sir!"

"We'll keep our mouths shut," Tom Moone said, "and our ears cocked for the sound of your drum. When you're ready to sail again, we'll be with you!"

Fran hefted a bag of gold. "It shouldn't be too long. I won't have to argue about what we can do. I can prove it!"

An hour later he set the bag of gold down with a thump on William Hawkins' desk. "There! I told you I'd make Philip of Spain pay for the voyage."

William had no answering smile. "Your escapades in the Caribbean have the country by the ears."

"What do you mean? Who talked?"

"The Spanish ambassador. He has complained to high heaven. Says their ships in the Caribbean have been having a terrible time of it. A certain devil—they call him '*El Draque*'—" William pronounced it in two syllables—"DRAH-kay." "—has been flitting about like a ghost. The Queen's council is in quite a turmoil. William Cecil—he's Lord Burghley now and very important—vows this 'El Draque' must be stopped."

"What does the Queen say?"

"I hear she offers sympathy to the Spanish ambassador, but declares she knows nothing of the marauder. Says that if they will catch El Draque and bring him to her she'll make him pay for his crimes."

Fran laughed. "But they'll have to catch him first?"

"Every minute you spend in the Caribbean—you're risking your life. You know that, don't you? There is no way the Queen can protect you."

"I haven't asked for protection!"

"And your crew?"

"They're ready to sail with me to the last man. And the next time we come home our ships will be ballasted with gold!"

William shook his head. "We can't possibly raise the force to attack a treasure fleet."

"Who said anything about attacking a treasure fleet? What about a raid on the storehouses on shore? Where the treasure is waiting to be picked up by the fleet? Here —let me show you." He sketched a map of the Caribbean and explained.

"Fran! That's the maddest, most reckless . . . How many ships do you want?"

They planned; they shook hands. Then Fran touched a candle to the corner of his map. As the paper flared he dropped it on the hearth. He waited, then scuffed the charred paper with his toe. "The safest place for maps," he said.

"You want to sail in May?"

Fran nodded. "That will put me there at the right time to strike. One quick raid, and we'll be back."

"I'll see about outfitting the ships," William said. "Now the men . . ."

"I'll pick them myself, one by one," Fran said. "They won't even know I'm considering them when I talk to them."

One afternoon in April Tom Moone appeared at Fran's cottage. "Captain Drake, a couple of lads turned up from London. Say they want to go with you on your next raid."

Fran jumped to his feet. "Who told them there'd be a raid?"

Tom shrugged. "Search me. They seemed almighty sure where you were going. What you want me to do with them?"

"Bring them here. If they're up to something, I'll know it. Then you can take care of them."

"Like so?" Tom drew a finger across his throat.

"Good Lord, no! Just arrange to keep them out of the way till after we sail!"

"Whatever you say, Captain Drake. Truss 'em up or cut 'em up, it's all one to me." He meandered off.

"Fran!" Mary's eyes were wide. "He means it! He'd kill them and not bat an eye!"

"If they were planning to kill me, what would you want him to do?"

Mary shivered. "How can you be sure what they're planning?"

"I've never misjudged a man yet. There's nothing to worry about."

"I'm not worried," Mary declared. But when Tom Moone knocked on the door she dropped a plate.

7

The raid on Nombre de Dios

Fran swung the door wide and looked out at the two young men. The first was short, well-knit, with dark red hair and a devil-may-care grin. The second was tall and fair, with a grave smile.

Fran gave a yell of delight and landed in the yard. "Joe! And Johnny!" And the three were slapping backs, shaking hands, and hugging each other.

Tom grinned at Mary. "His brothers."

"But I thought they were dead? His father's will—"

"Guess the old man disowned the sailing part of his family. Or maybe he thought they *were* dead. When a fellow's been gone at sea for a year or two, people at home never know whether he's alive or dead, do they?"

"No," Mary said slowly, "we never know."

"William Hawkins found them in London." Tom fished a letter from his pocket. "Here's a note about them. They wanted to surprise Captain Drake." He chuckled and ambled off.

Fran was still shouting joyously. "Come in! Come on in! Mary! It's Johnny and Joe!"

Johnny shook hands. Joe kissed her soundly on both cheeks. After supper the four of them sat around the table together.

Fran read William's note. "He gives you quite a recommendation, Johnny."

Johnny flushed. "Thank you."

"Doesn't say anything about you, Joe."

Joe grinned. "Johnny's the brains. I'm just muscle. I follow orders all right—when somebody's looking. But I've never done a lick of work I didn't have to. I can even make the other hands push me round the capstan when we're weighing anchor. And—"

Johnny interrupted. "Don't believe him, Fran. He's a fine sailor."

"But always before the mast. You got room in the fo'c'sle?"

"Just the spot for you," Fran said. "And the spot for you, too, Johnny. I'm taking two ships with me. The *Pasha* belongs to William, but the *Swan*—she's my own. Can I count on Captain John Drake to command her?"

"Aye, aye, sir!" was all Johnny said, but his eyes glowed.

"And you—" Fran doubled his fist and flicked Joe's chin. "I'll keep you with me on the *Pasha*."

"Plenty to eat?" Joe asked. "I'm a valiant trencherman."

"Philip of Spain fed us very well."

Joe laughed. "I heard he had about two hundred ships in the Caribbean."

Mary gasped. "Fran! You never told me that! How did you ever get out alive?"

"Perfectly simple," Fran said. "The Spanish have no conception of sea fighting. If they sight an enemy the only thing they know how to do is to run alongside and board her for a hand-to-hand fight. They fight with men. I fight with my ship."

Even Johnny and Joe looked puzzled.

"Like this." Fran stood a plate on edge. "This is a Spanish ship. Now, suppose the wind's coming from your direction, Joe. Broad on her starboard." He picked up a mug. "Here I am, keeping to windward of her, where I can maneuver. Now, supposing the wind was coming from your direction, Johnny—broad off her larboard. If I was still to starboard—"

"She'd act like a windbreak, wouldn't she?" Mary said.

The brothers cheered.

Mary was looking at the plate and mug. "Is that how much bigger a Spanish ship is?"

"Sometimes," Fran admitted.

"And you'll attack her?"

"Why not? I can maneuver around her like she was at anchor. My guns can shoot farther than anything she carries. One chain shot into her rigging and she generally strikes her colors."

Johnny explained, "Chain shot is a pair of cannon balls,

Mary, fastened together with a length of chain. They go whirling through the air. When they hit, they do a lot of damage."

"So the Spaniard strikes like a sensible fellow," Fran repeated.

"What if he didn't?" Mary asked. "What if he took after you and caught you and—"

Fran chuckled. "That's the rub. He'd have to catch me."

"Anyhow," Joe said, "this action isn't going to be a sea fight, is it? We're going to raid a town."

Confound it, Fran thought, why did he have to bring that up? I'd better explain it. If I don't, she'll worry.

Again he sketched a rough map of the Caribbean. "Here's the Spanish Main—the northern coast of South America. Here's the Isthmus of Panama—the narrow strip of land between the Caribbean and the Pacific. The town of Panama is on the Pacific coast. Nombre de Dios —we call it 'Nombre,'—is on the Caribbean. The Pacific fleet of the Spanish brings the treasure to Panama, then they send it across the mountains by mule train to Nombre. That's where the treasure fleet from Spain picks it up."

"Sounds like a lot of trouble," Joe remarked. "Loading and unloading ships. Don't they have an all-water route to the Pacific? By the Strait of Magellan?"

"Too dangerous," Fran said. "They lost so many ships that way that they gave it up. It got so they couldn't even get a captain to attempt the route. He knew if he said

'Strait of Magellan' he'd have a mutiny on his hands. So the Spanish had to build ships over there in the Pacific. They haven't sent a ship through the strait for years. All the treasure from Peru comes overland to Nombre."

"And that's where we take it, eh?" Joe chuckled. "Right into Nombre! Yelling like murder! That'll be fun!"

"Can we get our ships into Nombre Bay without being seen?" Johnny asked.

"Good boy, Johnny!" Fran said. Again he touched a candle to his map and watched it burn. "No, we couldn't. But I've had three pinnaces built and cut apart. We'll take them over, put them together when we get there, and use them for the raid. They are big enough to hold a goodly part of our men. Small enough to handle with oars if we're becalmed."

"I'll pray for a breeze," Joe said.

Johnny and Fran laughed with him.

Mary's smile was tender. "It's wonderful to see you three together."

"That's how you'll see us from now on," Fran said. "Together."

"I may be wearing a ball and chain sometimes," Joe remarked, "but I'll be along!"

They were together one night late in May of '72 when they ghosted out of Plymouth Harbor. They were together at dawn one morning in mid-July when the *Pasha* led the way through a narrow passage between two wooded capes, and a harbor stretched before them.

"We call it 'Hidden Harbor,'" Fran told Joe.

Tom studied the shore. "You sure this is the place, Captain Drake? No sign of the clearing we made for a camp."

"Had time to grow over," Fran said. "It's the place, all right. You'll know it when we find the stores we buried."

He led the way ashore to the cache of supplies—and stared at the holes in the ground.

"Guess our Hidden Harbor isn't hidden any longer," Tom said. "Where'll we go now?"

"We'll stay right here. Chances are the men who discovered our caches will never come back. They certainly won't expect us to stay here."

"If they do come back?" one asked.

"We'll be ready for them."

The palisade they build covered almost an acre. The logs of the wall towered thirty feet high.

"Thank goodness that's done!" Joe groaned. "Now we can do something easy—like raiding Nombre."

One night late in July the three pinnaces crept out of their hideaway and set sail for Nombre. Fran commanded the first, Johnny the second. Joe was in the third. Not in command—Tom Moone was in charge—but just, as Joe said, "to pray for steady breezes."

The second morning out they sighted an island. "A good place to water," Fran said, "if it's uninhabited."

They circled the island, found no sign of people, and pulled for the shore. Fran jumped from his pinnace and waded in, leaving his men to beach the boat. He stooped, crawled through a tangle of vines, straightened, and found himself confronted by two huge savages.

Their arms were raised, holding heavy knives over their heads—knives with blades as wide as a man's hand and almost a yard long. Machetes, Fran knew, and razor-keen.

One of the savages began to talk softly in a mixture of Spanish and some unknown tongue. For once the hated white man had been careless. He had forgotten to make them come to the beach, empty-handed, before he landed. Now he was in their power. His men could not save him. "We may die," he said through his teeth, "but you'll die first!"

I've got to make them believe I'm not Spanish! Fran thought. That I'm an enemy of the Spanish! "*No español,*" he said quietly. "*Enemigo del español!*"

Something flicked in the glaring eyes. Doubt? Suspicion? Or the beginning of belief?

His men would be ashore now. If they tried to do anything to rescue him . . . "Don't make a move!" he called. "They're enemies of Spain! They'll be our friends!"

He talked again to the savages. He was the enemy of Spain. He was the friend of any enemy of Spain. All his men were enemies of Spain.

The savages had not moved. Their machetes were still poised, and their eyes alert.

"All enemies of Spain!" he told them. "I am your friend. I am El Draque."

"El Draque!" The savages shouted the name. They rushed toward Fran, waving their knives. They circled about him, leaping and shouting, "El Draque!"

"They've heard of me, thank God," Fran called. "Lay down your weapons. Come in friendship. Bring food. We'll have a feast."

Over the feast he got the story of the men. They were of a tribe the Spanish called "*Cimaroons*," or just "*Maroons*." Many years before some Negro slaves—their ancestors—had escaped into the hills on the mainland and joined forces with the Indians.

Diego—who towered six-feet-six—was a chieftain. Antonio—a mere six-feet-two—was one of his men. Down through the years, Diego said, they had made war on the Spaniards. When they captured one . . . His giant hands were claws, his eyes burned, and his lips drew back in a snarl.

"At ease," Fran warned his men. "Diego's not threatening me. He's talking about the Spaniards." How did they happen to be on the island, he asked.

The Spanish had captured them. No, Diego said, the Spanish did not kill Maroons when they captured them. They needed workers. So they generally imprisoned a Maroon on a deserted island to clear land or fell trees. When the Spanish came to the island they never landed until all the imprisoned Maroons were standing on the beach, empty-handed.

Fran translated for his men. "I've promised to put

Diego and Antonio ashore on the mainland, so they can return to their people."

"Good!" Joe said. "One can have my oar!"

"They'll have seats of honor in my pinnace," Fran told him.

Two nights later they touched the mainland. Diego vowed friendship unto the death to El Draque. He and Antonio disappeared.

"Whew!" Joe gave a gusty sigh of relief. "I'm glad to see the last of them! By the time we caught up with you there wasn't a thing we could have done to—"

"Don't be so restless with your weapons," Fran said. "We have no enemies but Spaniards. Anybody else we meet in the Caribbean is sure to be a friend."

"If we have time to explain," Johnny remarked quietly.

By dawn they were hiding in a cove near Nombre Bay, waiting for night. Fran sketched the layout of Nombre de Dios and outlined the action. "We'll split into two parties. Half of you will go ahead, circle the town, ready to enter from the rear. The rest of us will enter here. You'll wait for my signal. When I blow my whistle we'll all start shooting and yelling. All the racket possible from both directions. They'll think they're surrounded by an army."

"When they find out they're not?" one asked.

"We'll be gone. Surprise and speed. That's the thing."

"What time will we attack?"

"Just at dawn," Fran said. "That's when they're most

off guard. It's so hot here they work at night and sleep by day."

When darkness had fallen they crept into Nombre Bay and settled down to wait for dawn.

After ten minutes the men stirred restlessly. A man behind Fran leaned forward. "How much longer?"

"Six hours." Fran heard the hiss of a quick-drawn breath. He reached back in the dark to touch the fellow's hand. Clammy. "Waiting's always hardest," he said. "You'll be all right when we're on the move."

"Y-y-y-yes, sir."

Another ten minutes . . . another . . . The moon rose. The shadows of the men took shape—tense, strained forward, listening. They weren't going to last till dawn.

"Be enough light by the moon." Fran whispered. "We're going in. Pass the word."

On shore he said, "Archers, test your bows."

Joe drew back on his bowstring. A good ninety-pound pull, he said. The proper weapon for an Englishman. Especially if he had brawn instead of brains. A whisper of a chuckle ran through the men.

Bless him, Fran thought, he's a godsend! He said, "Light your matches." He held out the one cord he had kept smoldering.

Each gunner held the end of his cord to it, blew on it until he had a light, and passed the fire on to the next one. When the first group were ready they moved off in the shadows, shielding the tips of their matches with their hands so the glow would not betray them.

Fran counted to five hundred slowly, then led his party toward the town square. His whistle shrilled, and the din that broke out almost made him jump.

The Spanish answered with a scattered fire. Something struck Fran's right thigh like a hammer blow. Then numbness deadened his leg. After a moment he knew his right foot was wet. A few more steps and his boot was filling with blood. Confound it! He forced himself not to limp.

Someone yelled, "El Draque!" The word ran through the square. The brief resistance ended. The key to the storehouse? *Sí! Sí!* A man stumbled in his haste to unlock the door. Two others scuttled in, holding up torches. Bars of silver were stacked higher than a man's head, in a pile longer than the keel of the *Pasha.*

"Bah! We've no use for silver! The keys to the gold and jewels!" Fran tried to bellow the words, but his voice sounded faint in his ears. He must have made more noise than he could hear, he decided. There was more *Sí! Sí!* and the Spaniards led the way to another storehouse.

Then a sudden downpour began.

"Take cover!" he yelled.

They scurried under the deep overhang of the roofs around the square. Fran leaned against a wall and closed his eyes. No—wouldn't do. Dizzier. He stiffened himself against the wall and forced his eyes to stay open. If only the downpour would end! They didn't dare move until it did. Damp powder and limp bowstrings would be useless. Nothing to do but wait . . . wait . . .

His thoughts grew fuzzy. He fought back to consciousness. The torrent ended as suddenly as it began. The moon came out from behind a cloud.

"Ready!" Fran yelled. He stepped forward. Then the moon blurred, the men blurred, and the stones of the square came up to meet him.

8

The end of the Swan

The next thing he heard was the creaking of oarlocks and the lapping of water. He felt the motion of the boat.

"What the devil?" He struggled to sit up.

"Please, Captain Drake, lie still! We're trying to stop the bleeding!"

"Did you get the treasure?"

"We did not! When you fainted we got out of there fast!"

He stormed at them. He struggled against their hands. But they held him down until they finished binding a pad against the wound.

What good would it do them to capture the treasure and lose him, they asked. What could they do without him to lead them? As soon as he recovered, they'd raid Nombre again. Next time they'd get the treasure, all right!

Fran did not answer. No use telling them yet that the plan would not work twice. The Spanish had been warned. By now messengers were dashing headlong over the mountain trails to Panama. Soldiers would swarm into Nombre to guard it. No chance for a second raid there. He'd have to have another plan . . . another . . . His thoughts grew fuzzy.

July ended. August was almost over. Fran stared at the walls of their palisade and searched his mind once more for a plan. His men were getting restless. Not that they said anything. He could feel it in the air—see it in their eyes. *Waiting gnaws at a man's heart.* Another two weeks, he thought grimly, and I'll have a problem on my hands!

"Beat to quarters!" a lookout yelled. "We're surrounded!" Men scurried to light matches, to grab up their guns and their bows and arrows.

Fran climbed to the lookout's perch, swept a glance at the forest, and laughed. "You idiot! They're Maroons." He called, "Open the gates!"

Four dozen Maroons entered the palisade, leaping and shouting, "El Draque! El Draque!"

Diego had heard of the trouble at Nombre. He had come to help El Draque. He had a plan.

"Good enough! A plan is what I need!"

Diego squatted and scooped earth into a long, narrow ridge. He laid a pebble on the south side of the ridge. "Panama." He laid another pebble on the north side of the ridge. "Nombre." With a stick he traced a twisting line over the ridge. "Mules."

"That's the path of the *recuas*—the mule trains—bringing the treasure from Panama to Nombre?" Fran asked.

Diego nodded. He traced another faint line that sloped up to hit the trail. "Ambush."

"You can lead us through the forest to a place of ambush?"

Diego could. His men would cut a path for El Draque.

"How long would it take us to cut our way?" Fran asked.

Diego spread five fingers. "Sleeps," he said. "Maybe more."

Five days and nights—maybe longer—through unbroken jungle. But anything was better than waiting. "We'll do it!" Fran said. "We'll start tomorrow!"

Diego shook his head. Not now. Rains coming. No mule trains until the rains ended. Must wait.

Another wait! Fran thought of the tense, anxious men in Nombre Bay. "How long?" he asked.

Once more Diego spread five fingers. "Moons," he said.

Moons! That meant months! Five months—until the end of January!

Long after the Maroons had gone Fran sat staring at nothing. Five months to survive in enemy territory, to feed his men, to hold them to their purpose. Five months—while the days and weeks gnawed at their hearts. When he told them what they faced . . . Well, no use standing off and on about it. He called them together.

"I'm glad you're the men I have with me. I don't know

six dozen other men in the world I'd want to depend on for what we're going to do."

He swept a glance over his Devon lads. Every blessed one of them was standing an inch taller.

"Diego and I have planned our next raid. We're going to have to wait a while before we can carry it out. That means Philip's ships are going to have to feed us longer than we thought."

The men were smiling now.

"We won't have too much work to do. You'll only be on duty every other day. On your free days we'll have bowling—archery—anything else you can think of. You may even loll against a tree and order a man who is on duty to bring you something to eat. Of course, the next day, when you're on duty and he's off . . ."

He waited for their laughter to die down so they could hear him.

"We'll arm two of the pinnaces with guns from the *Swan*. We'll use them to do our provisioning. We'll use the third pinnace for fishing, bringing firewood, and other less amusing work."

The men were still laughing when Johnny asked, "How long do we wait, sir?"

"Five months. Until the end of January."

The laughter stopped. The smiles faded.

Then Joe stretched and yawned. "Five months. A hundred and fifty days. That means seventy-five days off duty!"

They laughed again.

Tom got the signal in Fran's eyes and followed him to the middle of their bowling green. "Yes, Captain Drake?"

Fran glanced around. No one within earshot. "Keep your voice down, Tom. No matter what you think or want to say."

"Aye, aye, sir."

"There's a job to be done that only you can do."

"Anything you say, sir."

"For the next five months we'll do our raiding with the pinnaces. They are faster, and can disappear more easily —run into shallow water, where the Spanish can't follow them."

"Yes, sir!" Tom's grin was cheerful.

"But we can't man the *Pasha,* the *Swan,* and the pinnaces. We've got to get rid of the *Swan.* I want you to sink her."

"Captain Drake! She's the—"

"I know everything you can say about her. Didn't I plan her? Didn't I watch her a-building from the time her keel was laid? But she's got to go. You'll bore holes in the bottom—close to the keel as possible where they'll be hard to locate. By the time anybody notices anything, it'll be too late to save her."

Tom stretched out his big hands pleadingly. "Captain Drake, I said I'd do anything for you, but—"

"Then do it. Tonight."

"You—you don't want to think about it?"

"I have."

"But, Captain Drake—"

"It's an order, Moone!"

"Aye, aye, sir." Tom lumbered off, his head hanging.

At the first streak of dawn Fran looked toward the *Swan*. Yes, Tom had done his work. She was riding lower in the water. Poor Tom. And poor Johnny! He was so proud of his first command.

Mid-morning Fran proposed that he and Johnny go fishing. "I'll row out," he said. "Then you'll have to row back when we're loaded with fish." In the middle of the harbor he idled, keeping an eye on the state of the *Swan*.

"You and Joe are a lot alike," Johnny said. "Talk lazy, and work like fiends. I wish I were more like the two of you."

"More like us? How?"

"As brave."

"But you are, Johnny."

"No, I'm not. I've never been. Remember that night on the *Clarissa*? When we heard prowlers? You thought the whole thing was a lark. I was scared to death."

"But you were just a little lad, Johnny. Only eight."

"You were only ten."

"But what you did took courage, Johnny. After the long wait, when you didn't know what had happened, you came to help me."

"I was shaking in my boots."

"That's real courage, Johnny. To go ahead when you're

shaking in your boots. Don't you see?" For a moment he had forgotten the *Swan*. Now, when he remembered, he looked toward her and yelled. "Heaven help us! The *Swan!*" He turned the boat and raced back, shouting orders.

Tom Moone was first aboard the *Swan*. "Not a chance to save her, Captain Drake! Six feet of water in the hold! Only thing we can do is salvage what we can and burn her!"

Johnny fired her, himself. He watched her begin to burn. Then he wheeled and started off alone.

Fran called, "Captain John Drake!" Johnny turned. "You are now in command of the *Pasha!*"

"But what about you?"

Fran nodded toward one of the pinnaces. "I'll take command of that. I hereby christen her the *Marauder*."

"But she isn't built to cross the Atlantic. When we're ready to go home—"

"When I need another ship, Philip of Spain will provide it."

The men cheered and shouted.

"And now," Fran said, "if I had a dozen hearty volunteers, I'd take the *Marauder* out for a little marketing."

Every man volunteered. Fran chose a dozen and promised the others their turn. Off they went in the *Marauder*, out to the wooded capes that hid the entrance to the harbor. Then, after a lookout had climbed a tree and reported no sail on the horizon, they stood out from the harbor, speeding quickly away so they would not betray their hiding place.

The second day out they sighted a small Spanish frigate. She altered her course to challenge them. When she came within range of the *Marauder's* guns the pinnace wheeled, and fired. Chain shot hurtled into the rigging of the *Pieta*. The guns of the *Pieta* roared, but the shot fell short. The *Marauder* came about and loosed another blast into her rigging. The *Pieta* struck her colors.

Fran hailed her. "What's your cargo?"

Nothing but food. Beef and pork bound for Cartagena.

"We'll have ten casks!"

A boat put out from the *Pieta*, bringing the casks to the *Marauder*. Fran gave them a receipt: Ten casks of meat were missing, through no fault of the *Pieta's* commander.

"Go your way!" he ordered. "Don't try to follow me, or I'll sink you!"

The *Pieta* obeyed. The *Marauder* went home.

It was December—twelve weeks and twenty raids later —when the *Marauder* sighted a small Spanish frigate sailing toward Cartagena.

"She handles well," Fran said. "Just about the size of the *Swan*. . . . Not too long before we'll need another vessel."

"Shall we stop her, sir, before she reaches the harbor?"

"No. Perhaps tonight when she's at anchor, with only the harbor watch on the alert—" Fran grinned. "I doubt if they're very alert . . ."

That night the *Marauder* crept into the harbor and five men boarded the *Dolores.* It did not take long to overpower the watch and batten down the hatches.

At dawn, just beyond range of the Spanish guns protecting the harbor, the *Dolores,* flying English colors, sailed back and forth across the entrance. When the harbor was in an uproar she stood out to sea, towing the *Marauder* behind her.

A goodly ship. A goodly store of provisions. Some amusing dispatches. One was a warning to the authorities of Cartagena: El Draque was still in the Caribbean. All vessels should proceed with caution.

With the Spanish crew prisoners between decks they brought the *Dolores* into Hidden Harbor. They manned the shrouds of their prize and hailed the camp. There was no answering cheer.

Joe came out alone in one of the *Pasha's* boats to meet them. "You have prisoners?"

"We have!" Fran called cheerily. "And a ship. It's my Christmas present to myself. Johnny shall keep the *Pasha.*"

"I'd like to talk to you before you bring your prisoners ashore," Joe said.

Fran joined him in the boat and waited until Joe had pulled away from the ship. "What's wrong?"

"Johnny's dead."

9

Ambush

"Johnny's dead." After those words it was a long time before Joe could go on. "He had some of us out in the third pinnace after firewood. We sighted this little Spanish frigate. Richard Allan dared Johnny to challenge her. At first Johnny said it was silly—we weren't armed. But Richard smiled a sort of—you know—one-sided smile, and Johnny got mad. He challenged the frigate. She opened fire. Got Johnny and Richard, both. They died before we reached home."

"Johnny! Why in heaven's name would he—"

"I remember what he said before he challenged her. 'No man shall report to my brother that I was hindermost in courage.' I guess that's the answer. All his life he'd been trying to measure up to you—to be as dashing—as reckless."

"But I'm not reckless!"

"No?" Joe's smile was crooked. "El Draque—the terror of the Caribbean—where the Spanish have more ships than he has men. Where—"

"That's just it, Joe! I can't afford to be reckless. Don't you understand?"

"Afraid I don't." He sat a moment, teeth clenched, eyes stony. "We buried them at sea. I knew that was what Johnny would want."

"I'll leave the prisoners on board the *Dolores* until I've talked to our men."

"I don't envy you the job, sir."

Fran talked first of the power and the wideflung dominions of Spain and Portugal—and of the one small island that was England. "We're not here on a dashing lark," he said. "We're here to prove that it's possible to strike a telling blow against Spain! That if we cut the lifeline to Philip's gold supply he'll topple on his throne!"

His men started to cheer.

"*Silence!*"

They stared at him. It was so still he could hear the lapping of water, the hum of insects.

"We are just six dozen men in the midst of the enemy. If we expose ourselves by reckless action we'll be destroyed. Mark this down and remember it! I'll not have reckless action! There will be no attack unless I order it! Do you hear me?"

They nodded.

"Why do you think I spent months exploring the Caribbean before I planned the raid on Nombre? Why do you think I took time to build this palisade so we'd be safe from attack? Why do you think we're waiting all these months before another raid on the treasure? Are these the acts of a reckless man?"

They shook their heads. They did not venture to speak.

"Obey orders, and there is no reason for us to lose another man. Do you understand?"

Again they nodded.

"We have prisoners aboard the *Dolores.* They'll be with us until we are ready to leave the Caribbean. And mark this down! They'll not be harmed! You're dismissed."

The men scattered. Joe came to Fran, holding out his hand.

"Forgive me?"

"There's nothing to forgive."

"Johnny's death hit me hard," Joe said. "We'd been together so long. We—" Head bowed, he fought for control.

It hit me just as hard, Fran thought. I'd been alone so long. But he spoke crisply. "Choose ten men. We'll bring the prisoners ashore."

Joe straightened. "Aye, aye, sir. I wish," he added, "that you could handle mosquitoes like you can handle men. They're driving us crazy."

Fran snorted. "Mosquitoes! If they're the worst problem we have to face . . . Choose your men!"

On board the *Dolores* he ordered, "Come out, one at a time, with your hands up!"

Luis Roderiguez, the captain, stalked out, disdaining

to raise his hands. But his men groveled and begged for mercy.

"You're safe here," Fran said. "I'm no Spaniard, killing men under a flag of truce."

Roderiguez flushed. Evidently he had heard of San Juan de Ulloa.

When they entered the palisade Tom Moone approached them.

"Please, Captain Drake, ask their commander if he knows anything to do about mosquitoes. These last two weeks . . ."

Roderiguez' lip curled at the question. Mosquitoes were merely one of the nuisances of the region. They seemed to bother newcomers more than the men who *belonged.* His men scorned to notice anything so insignificant. If the English could not endure them, perhaps they should give up and go home.

Fran clenched his teeth, counted to ten, and wished the last weeks of waiting were over.

At dawn a few days later Henry Chase, their doctor, wakened him. "Captain Drake, we've got some very sick men."

"What is it?"

"I don't know, sir. I've never seen anything like it. Violent pain. Raging fever. Out of their heads."

"Not the plague? Dear God, not the plague!"

"No, they don't have the look of men with the plague.

Some of them are turning yellowish. I think we'd better isolate them. If this spreads through the camp . . ."

That day one man died. The next day thirty were sick, and another died.

"We call it *fiebre amarilla*—yellow fever," Roderiguez said. "It seems to bother newcomers more than the men who *belong*. I suggest, Captain Drake, that you'd better have the men who are still hale dig graves—while they are able to dig them. A long time ago we learned the wisdom of being beforehand with the graves."

"Dig graves and have them ready? As though every man who gets sick is doomed? That's the most fiendishly cold-blooded thing I ever heard of!"

Roderiguez lifted an eyebrow. "Odd attitude for a pirate."

Fran grabbed him by the throat, and then released him. "I'm not a pirate. If I were, you'd be dead. There'll be no beforehand graves here, waiting for men to die!"

But Roderiguez had been right. When sixty men were stricken, the dozen still on their feet could not care for the living and bury the dead.

Roderiguez was elaborately polite when he offered help. El Draque, he said, had lived up to his reputation for being merciful to prisoners. It would be his men's pleasure to assist in the digging of graves.

With Tom Moone and Joe to guard them the prisoners marched out each morning to bury those who had died in the night. Then there was a morning when only Tom Moone guarded them, and they dug Joe's grave. Another morning when they buried the doctor.

When the rains ended only thirty-one Englishmen had survived. Ten of those lay tossing and muttering.

"Diego will be coming any day," Tom Moone said. "What'll we do?"

"Raid the mule trains!" Fran told him.

"With how many men, sir?"

"If necessary," Fran declared, "you and I could do it alone."

Tom smiled briefly, then said, "I think one of us better stay here at the camp to—well, hold things together. Our lads have had about all they can take."

"They'll feel better when Diego comes."

There was panic among the prisoners when the Maroons appeared. Forty towering savages, armed with spears, blowguns, and machetes. Even Roderiguez turned white.

And, at the sight of the hated Spanish, a guttural murmur ran through the band of Maroons. Fran talked to them through Diego—not all the Maroons understood Spanish. Fran could only hope that Diego was translating what he said. He was El Draque. He never killed women, children, or unarmed men. Diego and his men would follow El Draque's way. The murmur died, but forty pairs of eyes still burned.

"I'll take thirty Maroons with me," Fran told Tom, "and fourteen of our men. I'll leave the other ten Maroons here with you. In the excitement of an attack on the Spaniards I'll probably have my hands full with thirty."

"We'll have our hands full with ten," Tom said, "but we'll try to keep them in hand."

"*You must!* Remember, a hundred men from the *Minion* may be in Spanish hands. Our reputation for mercy to prisoners may save their lives."

"And may not. For all we know they're dead now."

"You'll guard the prisoners, Moone!"

"Aye, aye, sir."

Roderiguez watched as Fran's men and the Maroons readied the *Pasha* and two pinnaces for sea. He watched as thirty Maroons went aboard—some to the pinnaces, and some to the *Pasha.* "Captain Drake! You'll not risk the lives of your men with those savages!"

"What's the risk?" Fran asked. "They're not Spaniards."

Outnumbered two to one by the Maroons, he sailed. Diego and half of his men squatted on the deck of the *Pasha,* whetting their machetes.

Edward Pike had as much courage as the next Devon man, but he wet his lips. "I'd feel a lot better, Captain Drake, if they didn't have those knives."

"Be glad they do. Those are machetes—best tool in the world to hack a path through the jungle."

"Oh, *tools!*" Edward sounded relieved. "I thought they were weapons."

Yes, Fran thought, they probably use them for social purposes, too. But he didn't say what he was thinking.

Diego piloted them to a bay surrounded by jungle that shut out the sky. He spoke to his men, giving orders no white man could understand. Half waded ashore with their machetes and began hacking at the tangle of vines. They disappeared into the green gloom. The other Maroons made packs of all supplies, shouldered their burdens, and waded in. They, too, disappeared.

Empty-handed excepting for their weapons the men of Devon followed. They paused a moment to look back at the familiar shapes of ship and boats. Then they entered the unknown world of the jungle.

For a time they stumbled and clawed their way across level land. Then the path grew steep and they were forced to climb. After six hours two of the men sprawled on the ground and said they could go no farther. Diego shouted to his men. Four of them loaded their packs on their companions and carried the two Devon lads for an hour.

The third day they had left the muggy heat of the lowlands behind them. The air had a brisk tingle. Up . . . up . . . What had Diego said about the time it would take to reach the place of ambush? "Five days—maybe more." Quite a few more, evidently. After a week they were still climbing.

The eighth day Diego said, "Come, El Draque, I show you."

He led the way to a huge tree with steps built up the side. Fran climbed until the leafy branches hid both ground and sky and he was alone in a green world. Finally he reached a large platform, big enough to hold ten men. Around the platform, to north and south, someone had cut away branches.

To the north, down below wooded slopes, Fran saw the Caribbean. He turned to the south and caught his breath. There lay the limitless blue of the Pacific.

He knelt. "Almighty God! Give me life and leave to plow those waters once with an English ship!" At last he spoke to Diego. "My men must see this. Send them up, half at a time."

Long after they had returned to the ground and were on their way again his men walked in silence. Downhill now—toward Panama. They made a wide detour to skirt the mountain town of Venta Cruz, then Diego led them for the first time to the trail that crossed the mountains. Here, he said, was the place for the ambush.

He sent one of his men toward Panama to reconnoiter. Then the Maroons squatted on the trail, motionless. Fran tried to imitate their pose and their calm, but in an hour he had fidgeted to another position so many times he had lost count.

Suddenly Diego lifted his head and made a warning gesture. The Maroons crouched and disappeared into the undergrowth. Fran's men followed.

An interminable wait. Then they heard the *tlot-tlot* of

hoof beats coming from the direction of Venta Cruz. They could see the horseman, bending forward in his saddle, gun ready, match smoldering. Quite on the alert. Ready for anything. But he passed almost four dozen men without knowing they were there. When the *tlot-tlot* faded toward Panama, Diego nodded. They returned to the trail. Once more the Maroons were motionless.

Toward evening Diego's scout was back. Tonight was the time. Two *recuas* were leaving Panama. More than a hundred mules. Some loaded with provisions, but many with silver, and four with gold and jewels. Better yet, the treasurer of Lima and his daughter were traveling with the mule train! Fourteen mules they had! Much treasure!

At dusk Fran told his men, "Take off your coats and shirts. Wear your shirts loose, over your coats. The flapping white will identify us to each other when the attack starts."

Where would the guards ride? he asked Diego. A vanguard and a rear guard, Diego said. The mules between. Fran positioned his men along the trail. Too bad, he thought, that he could not keep them bunched, close under his control. But they must be able to challenge the guards at both ends of the train.

"Remember! Not a sound—not a move—till I blow my whistle!"

They promised and went to take their positions.

Darkness. The minutes were hours. Diego touched Fran's arm. Fran listened. Nothing. Finally he heard it—

the faint tinkle of bells. The mule trains!

He tensed for the attack. After another dragging wait he forced himself to relax. The *recuas* must be crawling! The sound of the bells was no louder.

The moon rose, dappling the trail with silver light and leafy shadows.

Again Diego touched Fran's arm. Why? The bells were still far off. Presently he heard it—the *tlot-tlot* of hoof beats. Another lone rider from Venta Cruz, going toward Panama. Fran crouched lower, where he could see through the branches as the rider approached.

A sudden commotion—a flapping white shirt in the moonlight—and someone yelled and grabbed at the horse's bridle. The horse reared, whinnied, then pounded down the trail toward Panama. A Maroon jumped from the shadows and dragged the man with the flapping shirt out of sight.

Fran strode up the trail to check. It was Edward Pike, they told him.

"He said he was cold, and I gave him some brandy," one said. "I guess he's not used to it."

"Tie him and gag him!"

Fran returned to his post . . . and the wait.

The mule bells were louder now. The *recuas* came in sight—first the guards—then the mules—then more guards. Diego's scout had made a mistake. Not more than fifty mules—just one mule train.

Fran's whistle shrilled. His men leaped to the attack.

The guards immediately threw down their guns and raised their hands. One spoke English. "We surrender!" he shouted. "We surrender!"

With glad yells the men fell on the packs and began to open them.

"Nothing but food tonight," the guard said. "A rider from Venta Cruz warned us. Our captain sent the supply packs to spring the trap. The treasure has returned to Panama. Really no use to wait," he added. "When the *recuas* come again they will be very heavily armed."

10

Panic

Fran gave command with a jerk of his head. His band faded into the forest. Edward was still gagged, and his hands were tied behind him.

"Release him."

Edward staggered off, retching. Presently the sounds stopped. He came back to face the silence, the set jaws, of his comrades.

His knees shook and his feet dragged, but he forced himself to keep on until he stood before Fran. "Captain Drake, I know what you're going to do to me. I don't blame you. I deserve it. I ask just one thing, sir. When I face the firing squad, let me give the command."

"Who decided you should be shot?" Fran asked. The angry stares of the men turned on him. Fran gave them glare for glare. "If I shot every man who had disobeyed a command, I'd have killed the lot of you after our raid on Nombre. When you panicked just because I fainted, and gave up! Remember?"

Shame-faced smiles replaced the glares.

"But what'll we do, sir?" Edward asked. "I've ruined our chances. We'll never be able to take the mule trains now. They'll be too heavily guarded. And we'll never—"

"Save your breath for the trail," Fran said. "You'll need it. We've got to get out of here fast." To Diego he said, "Set a smart pace."

Diego did. Sure-footed, tireless, the Maroons trotted along, with the white men straggling, panting, in the rear.

When Fran called a halt his men sprawled where they were and slept. He lay with his eyes closed, but not sleeping. What could he do now? How would he put the dash and daring and spirit back into his men? The long wait had been enough to try the stoutest heart. And now—another failure. What could he do? Round and round, like rats in a maze, his thoughts scurried, finding no way out.

If he could take all thirty-one men on the raid . . . But he could not. Some must be there to guard the prisoners. He could not release them until he was ready to leave the Caribbean. Only thirty-one men . . . if he still had thirty-one . . .

When the first man stirred and sat up, Fran jumped to his feet. "Let's go!"

Up and up to the divide, then down and down through the jungle. The path they had made coming up had disappeared. Already the rank jungle growth had strangled it. Once more the machetes must slash and hack the way.

The heat laid heavy hands on them, sapping what heart they had left.

"What if our boats are gone?" one said. "And the *Pasha?*"

He's reading my mind! Fran thought. But he shrugged. "Why worry about what's before us? We left our troubles behind. The soldiers from Panama." He smiled. "Far behind us, I'd say! They could never keep the pace we've set for them!"

He put a little swagger back into them, but the doubt was still there. *What if the* Pasha *was gone?* The last sweltering miles were the longest. The last half mile. The last rods. Then whoops and yells as the men sighted their vessels and ran into the water.

Thank God something had lifted their spirits—for the moment. *But what next?*

As they weighed anchor he said, "We'll do a little provisioning on the way back. Courtesy of Philip!"

Diego's men smiled as they whetted their machetes. Fran's lads smiled as they checked their guns.

"Sail ho-o-o-o!" the lookout called. "Dead ahead! A pretty big one, sir. More than a hundred tons."

"Good! We'll do all our marketing in one fell swoop!"

After a time the lookout reported, "She's flying French colors, sir."

French colors? An ally? Or a Spanish trick?

"Ready with chain shot," Fran ordered, "but hold your fire till I give command!"

The *Pasha* sped to the meeting. Yes, the ship was big enough. More than a hundred tons.

Keeping to windward Fran brought the *Pasha* within gun range. "Strike! Or I send you to the bottom!"

The colors came down. The captain hailed them. "Monsieur, are you by any chance Captain Drake?"

"I am! El Draque!"

"Thank the good God I found you! I am Captain Têtu, a Huguenot. We need supplies desperately, monsieur. Above all—water!"

A Huguenot? If that were true he was a Protestant of France. He would be an ally. The accent was French . . . but an educated man of any nationality might know French . . .

"Run alongside her," Fran ordered, "but stand by your guns."

One look at the men of the *Ninon,* and there was no doubt about their condition.

"Bring water," Fran said. He boarded the *Ninon* and handed the first cup to Têtu.

"May the good God bless you," Têtu said. He knelt by one of his men, lifted his head, and held the cup to his lips.

"Break out five casks!" Fran called.

His men left their guns, shouldered the kegs, and boarded the *Ninon* to care for the crew.

"We don't have too much food with us," Fran said, "but we'll share what we have. We can always get more."

"They cannot eat too much for a time," Têtu said. "They have starved too long. We were not ready for sea when we fled from France."

"Fled? I thought the Huguenots had a truce with—"

"You have been long out of touch, monsieur. You have not heard of the Massacre of St. Bartholomew's Day, last August twenty-four. By courtesy of our queen mother, Catherine de' Medici."

"Another 'Bloody Mary'?" Fran asked. "In three years our Queen Mary had three hundred Englishmen burned at the stake."

"Three thousand Huguenots were murdered in Paris alone," Têtu said. "Throughout France, only the good God knows how many. Twenty thousand had died before we escaped, and the massacre was still going on. Philip of Spain sent his congratulations." Têtu spoke quietly, but hatred burned in his eyes.

Fran's mind was made up. "How many men have you?"

"Seventy."

"I have thirty-odd. Would you like to join forces with me?"

"Nothing could please me more!"

"I am at war with Philip of Spain."

Têtu's eyes widened. "Indeed? I had not heard that England—"

"This is personal. The vanguard action."

"Between us—a hundred men. With that force you will attack—"

"We won't need that many. As soon as your men recover their strength, and I do a little marketing—that won't take long . . ." I hope it won't take long! he thought. From now until we leave the Caribbean more than a hundred and fifty mouths to feed!

When the *Pasha* and the *Ninon* entered Hidden Harbor both rode low in the water. A shout from the palisade greeted them.

A grinning Tom Moone came out to meet them. All their men had recovered, he said. All the prisoners were still alive. He looked at the *Ninon*. "More prisoners?"

"Allies."

Evidently Têtu could read the doubt in Tom's eyes. "You think you can persuade your men, Captain Drake?" he asked.

"In five minutes!" Fran declared.

It did not take that long. Two minutes to tell what happened at the ambush—thirty seconds to remind them of what happened at Nombre de Dios. "All the way back from the ambush," he said, "I prayed for reinforcements! And we have them!"

His men cheered and fell to unloading provisions.

"Monsieur," Têtu said, "I am ready to believe all I have heard of El Draque. A commander who can fail—wait all those months—and fail again—and still have his men cheering—he is invincible!"

"I'd be the first to admit it!" Fran said. He called Diego

and the three made their plans. This time they would ambush the mule trains at the other end of the trail—just above Nombre.

"The Spanish will never dream that we'd dare to strike there," he said. "Surprise and speed. That will do it. Choose twenty of your strongest men. We'll be coming out faster than we go in!"

He left Têtu to choose his party and went to talk to his own men. "Tom Moone goes with me this time. You others—if you know you can march twenty-four hours without rest—may draw lots. But, unless you can stand the pace, don't volunteer."

Edward Pike drew first. "I get to go!" He must have felt the silence. He looked pleadingly at Fran.

Fran nodded. "Good enough. Without brandy you're one of the best. And I have had trouble with men who were sober." He whipped a smiling glance around. The men laughed. Even Edward. Then he walked quickly away. Only Fran, who was facing him, saw the tears in his eyes.

Fifteen English, twenty French, and thirty Maroons sailed with the *Pasha* and the pinnaces. They found cover for the *Pasha* in a small bay six miles from the river they would ascend. In the pinnaces they sailed across open water, then rowed as far up the river as the pinnaces could go. They drew lots for the men who would take the pinnaces back to their hiding place. Fran put Ellis Hixson in charge.

"We'll be two days overland to the ambush," Fran said, "and two days back. Meet us here Thursday afternoon. We'll need to get away fast."

"Thursday afternoon, sir! Without fail!" Ellis Hixson promised. The pinnaces started downstream.

The raiders faced the unbroken jungle. The Maroons led the way with their machetes. All day, through the steaming heat they scrambled on.

"Not fast enough," Diego said. "Night march, too."

With only a brief rest every hour they slogged ahead. At dusk Tuesday evening they reached their ambush on the trail above Nombre. They were so near the town they could hear the hammers and mallets of the workmen.

He and two of his men would guard them while the others slept, Diego said.

Fran translated his offer. "A good idea," he added. "We'll have to go back by forced marches, too. And we'll be heavy laden—I hope."

He saw Têtu's men eye the Maroons, and his boys studying the French. Not much trust in one another. He stretched out and closed his eyes. If he had misplaced his trust he'd have been dead long ago.

Diego's hand wakened him. "They come."

Fran made the rounds, waking the sleepers, then gave them their orders. "Remember! Not a move till I blow my whistle. Then—*move fast!*"

The men nodded. They lighted their matches and took

their positions. Almost dawn. Below, in Nombre, the hammers stopped. Silence. On the trail silence, too. Then they heard the first faint tinkle of the mule bells.

A dragging wait. Then the vanguard of the mule train. Fran waited until it was abreast the forward part of his ambush. His whistle shrilled.

The Spanish guards fired one volley, then broke and fled toward Nombre. Two Frenchmen were dead, and Têtu was wounded. Two of his men knelt by him. The others helped open the mule packs.

No lack of treasure this time. So much they could not possibly carry it. They buried tons of silver in crab holes in the river bank. Just the gold and jewels would be a burden.

Fran left them organizing the packs and knelt by Têtu.

"Through the left thigh," one of his men, Henri, said. "But I don't think it hit the bone. We've stopped the bleeding. We're going to make a litter—"

"You'll leave me here!" Têtu commanded. His men protested, but he was adamant.

"Then, sir, the two of us are staying with you!" And Henri and his companion carried their captain to a sheltered spot and sat down beside him.

Têtu looked up at Fran. "Captain Drake, what do you do with men like these?"

"I salute them!" He saw that the three were well supplied with water, food, and ammunition. He promised a rescue party.

"After you get back to Hidden Harbor," Têtu said. "Let the hunt die down."

They said good-by. Then, every man loaded down with treasure, they started the forced march back. All day, through the steaming heat. All night, by flickering torches. Lights were a risk, they knew, but any delay was more of a risk. Thursday a storm broke with the fury that only a tropical downpour could have.

"Thank God it won't rain this hard very long!" one gasped.

But it did.

Hour after hour, blinded by the downpour, they stumbled on. Shorter rests and longer marches. Only they weren't marches. They were stumbling sprawls forward.

Late Thursday afternoon they reached their rendezvous and stared, appalled, at the aftermath of the storm. Here, where the river had been too shallow for their boats, a muddy stream leaped and roared toward the ocean, carrying uprooted trees in the torrent. No sign of the pinnaces.

One man climbed a tree to look toward the ocean. He came down wild-eyed and shaking. "It's all over, sir! We're lost! No sign of our boats! But right down there—just beyond the mouth of the river—are seven Spanish pinnaces, loaded with men!"

11

Exile

For the first time Fran saw his men in a complete panic. They were lost! The Spanish would capture their boats and the *Pasha!* They were trapped! Their escape cut off! They would be hunted down like animals! Not a one of them would get out alive! They would—

"You whimpering curs!" Fran bellowed. "You dastardly milksops! You're a disgrace to Devon!" When he had shocked them into momentary silence, he said, "Save your breath. Let's get to work."

"But what can we do, sir?" Edward asked. "Look at that river! It's torn whole trees out by the roots!"

"That's our good luck," Fran said. "Saves having to cut them down. We're going to make a raft. And I'm going to find our pinnaces."

By morning they had made a raft—such as it was. Four saplings for oars, one for a sweep to steer it, and one for a mast. Their sail was a biscuit sack.

"It won't hold more than four of us," Fran said, "and we've got to be strong swimmers."

"Please, Captain Drake!" Edward begged.

Fran nodded to him and to a pair of Frenchmen who swore they could swim like fish—if they had to. The four stripped to their trousers and bare feet. If the raft capsized, Fran said, they'd have a better chance. The Frenchmen looked at the river, shrugged, and smiled.

"With God's help," Fran promised, "I'll find our pinnaces. And with God's help I'll set you all safe aboard the *Pasha!*"

His men said, "Aye, aye, sir. We'll pray for you." They eyed the swollen river.

The four of them climbed onto the raft. It submerged until they were in water up to their knees. They shoved off, and the raging torrent bore them downstream. What would they face when they reached the ocean? Would the current hurl them straight into the clutches of the Spaniards? If only there were some way to control the headlong speed of the lurching raft! But there was not. They could only hang on, try to keep their balance, and pray.

Into the sea. No sign of the Spanish boats. The four glanced at each other, started to smile, then gasped as the first wave washed over them, burying them to their shoulders, and tearing away their sail.

No headlong speed now. Every wave threatened to sweep them off the raft. Between waves, the sun broiled their naked backs—a sun so hot that it forced the men of Nombre to work by night. For nine hours they fought their way through the sea. Nine hours—while the merciless sun climbed to its zenith and began to sink. It was almost sunset when they caught sight of their pinnaces, struggling to make headway in the teeth of the wind.

"No wonder they couldn't get there," Edward gasped. "They can't do a thing with their oars in this sea!"

"They've got to," Fran said.

The pinnaces had not sighted the raft. Fran saw Ellis Hixson signal to his men—saw them give up the hopeless struggle and put into a little cove.

By the time the raft reached the cove, Hixson's men were sitting slumped around a campfire.

"Hixson!" Fran yelled. "No time for that! Launch the boats!"

Ellis and his men jumped to their feet and stared unbelieving.

"Bear a hand," Fran ordered. "We've got to get upstream for the men. Now!"

"But, sir, until the wind changes or the waves quiet down the pinnaces can't—"

"We've got to."

"But, sir—"

Edward Pike mocked him, " 'But, sir!' I'll show you how to handle a boat, you—" He started toward the beach, then collapsed and lay shivering.

"One of your men will stay here with the three of them," Fran said. "Keep them warm. They're badly burned. Let's go."

"But, sir, what about you?" Ellis asked. "You're just as badly—"

Fran glared at him. "I'm going with you. If you can't get anything out of your band of milksops, maybe you need a *man* in charge!"

Ellis flushed. "If we promise you, sir, to make every effort—"

"You'll 'make every effort,' all right!" Fran snarled. "I'll see to that! Bear a hand!"

By dawn they were halfway upstream, but the spent crew were beyond fighting another foot of the way against the current. Fran had used every epithet he could think of through the night. A few new ones occurred to him now. His men clenched their teeth; they smoldered. But they summoned one last measure of strength from somewhere, reached the rendezvous, and hailed the men on shore.

With cheers and yells the waiting men waded out to drag in the boats. "How'd you do it?" one asked. "We didn't look for you for at least two days! How'd you ever bring the boats upstream against that—"

"Captain Drake helped us 'make every effort,' " Ellis said through his teeth.

When they were safely aboard the *Pasha,* and under way, Fran went to his cabin. How long since he had slept? No use trying to lie down. Not with the burn he had. He sat on a chair, put a folded coat on the edge of his table, rested his forehead against it, and closed his eyes. Tired as he was, sleep did not come. Têtu . . . must send a rescue party. Send the *Pasha* and the pinnaces for him. Send plenty of men—in case the silver was still there. . . . Careen and trim the *Dolores* for the voyage to Plymouth . . . needed another small vessel . . . leave the *Pasha* . . . could not man her now . . . forty-two men lost . . . forty-two . . . At last he slept.

The *Dolores* and another small frigate they renamed the *Mary* were both ready for sea when the *Pasha* and the pinnaces returned from the attempt to rescue Têtu. Only Henri had been found. The Spaniards had captured the other two, and had dug up all the silver.

"For you, Captain Drake." Henri gave Fran a note, scrawled with the juice of some berry on the back of a letter of Têtu's. Fran read the first part of it aloud:

> *I have ordered Henri to get away if possible. He will be obeying orders and not deserting me. . . .*

He scanned the rest of the note, and stopped reading aloud:

> *I deem it the greatest privilege of my life, Captain Drake, to have spent these days with you. I consider you the most gallant soul, the most valiant warrior, and the kindliest man I have ever known. . . .*

Kindly? Fran thought of all the things he had said to his men—the ones who panicked when the boats failed to meet them—Hixson and his poor lads when he had browbeaten them through the impossible seas and upstream to the rendezvous.

André, one of the Frenchmen who had been on the raft, said, "Ah, our Captain Têtu was the greatest commander who ever lived! At times of a sternness—a magnificent sternness! No one could match his words when he—"

Bedlam broke out among the browbeaten lads from Devon. Hadn't André heard anything Captain Drake said to them? Proudly they shouted every epithet Fran had hurled at them. There! Had Captain Têtu ever equaled that?

André shook his head. "Never, my friends. I did not realize your language offered such magnificent possibilities!" His glance met Fran's with a twinkle.

Two days later, when the *Ninon's* crew weighed anchor with their half of the treasure, they manned the shrouds and cheered for El Draque.

Diego and his men sailed next, in the pinnaces, loaded with presents.

Then Fran ordered the sails removed from the *Pasha,* took them ashore, and presented them with a flourish to Luis Roderiguez. "The *Pasha* is yours, *señor,*" he said. "Some slight return for detaining you so long."

Before Roderiguez had recovered from his astonishment, Fran was aboard the *Mary,* yelling, "Heave around!" The *Dolores* and the *Mary,* ballasted with treasure, stood out of Hidden Harbor.

Tom Moone looked back with narrowed eyes. "The *Pasha* can outsail us, sir."

"Not till they bend on her sails, Moone!"

When they were entering the English Channel Fran opened a chest of gold and began to make packets of coins, writing a man's name on each: John Drake, Captain . . . Joseph Drake, seaman . . . Henry Chase, ship's doctor . . . He stopped and sat with his head in his hands. *How many came back? Sticks in a man's craw. . . .* But there was a memory older than those words. Adam Tanner's challenge: You whimper about a hard life at sea! What'd be so easy about life under the heel of a conqueror?

Maybe now the Queen and her council would believe they did not have to kneel to Spain. He'd make them understand. "There is only one defense!" That's what he'd say to them. "We must attack! And we can!"

He straightened and went on with his task.

As they entered Plymouth Harbor they heard church bells. Fran sent Edward Pike ashore. "Go to the church, find Mrs. Drake, and tell her very quietly that I'm back. But don't disturb the service!"

"Aye, aye, sir!"

Fran called all his men to the *Mary* and knelt in prayer with them. From the shore came a swelling murmur. He looked up. The whole congregation had poured out of the church and was coming down to the harbor!

Edward returned, full of apologies. "The church was crowded, sir, and I didn't want to disturb them. You said not to disturb them, sir. So I asked a man in a back pew to pass the word to Mrs. Drake. Just so I wouldn't disturb them, sir!"

A boat was approaching the ship, and Mary was waving.

Tom Moone saluted. "If I might go ashore, sir, maybe I could answer their questions?"

When Mary and Fran emerged from the cabin, all his men but the harbor watch had gone ashore, and most of the crowd had scattered. The only townspeople who stopped them said, "Sorry to hear about your brothers, Captain Drake."

"God bless Tom Moone!" Fran said. "I'll see them all this week—but one at a time." He and Mary walked home in peace.

"Do you remember your Uncle Robert Drake?" she asked.

"I heard Father speak of him."

"He died and left an orphaned son. Jack's ten. He's come to live with us."

"He wasn't at church with you?" he frowned. "What sort of bringing up has he had?"

"He loves to ride," Mary said. "Sometimes he goes off before sunrise and doesn't come back for hours. He's never done it on Sunday, though. He's a dear boy, Fran. A good boy. He always minds me. If I tell him not to do something, he never does. But—"

Fran grinned. "He does so many things you never thought of? Don't worry. I'll take that young rapscallion in hand. He's probably home by now. I'll give him a talking-to that—"

Jack was not there. In the middle of the afternoon a neighbor's boy brought a smudged note:

Dear Cousin Mary

I heard the news. I think it would be nice for you and Captain Drake to have his first day at home without extra people around. Even me. I have gone over to stay with Cousin William Hawkins.

Your obedient servant

J. Drake

"Well, I'll be . . . Don't ever worry about that lad, Mary. He's a gentleman and a scholar."

It was nine that night when William Hawkins turned up at their door with a smiling welcome—and worried eyes.

"What's wrong?" Fran asked.

Mary gasped. "Jack! He's—"

And, because he was worried, Fran roared, "What's that young scoundrel done now?"

"Jack? Why, nothing. He's over at my place. Been in

bed for an hour. No, Fran, you're the 'young scoundrel' we've got to worry about."

"What do you mean?"

"Affairs with Spain are in a very difficult state. Unless you're gone before word reaches London . . . Well, you've just got to be gone. That's all."

"Where to?"

"It's better for you to sail under sealed orders. At dawn. The *Falcon* is waiting for you behind St. Nicholas's Island. She's provisioned and manned." He gave Fran a paper, folded and sealed. "Only five men in the world know where you're going. That could be four too many. There's a price on your head."

"My ships?"

"I've had them moved to a safer place. We'll keep in touch with you. I'll take care of your cargo, pay off your crews, and give you a strict accounting. And I'll take care of Mary and Jack, too. I'm sorry, Fran. I know it's disappointing."

"It's idiotic! If I have proved we can strike at Spain—"

"Fran, you're a master mariner, and a brilliant fighter. But you're no statesman."

"Does the Queen think her statesmen can save her from Philip?"

"Don't ever underestimate Her Majesty, Fran. She came to the throne of a debt-ridden, beleaguered country. She swore she'd take care of us. And she's done it! For almost fifteen years! She may make her maneuvers over the council table—moves we can't understand. She may twist and turn, promise and change her mind, till she drives foreign princes half crazy—and her own advisers, too. But she's kept the peace. And England is far better off than when she came to the throne."

"How nice that'll be for Philip," Fran growled, "when he decides to take over the country. How long am I to be banished?"

"We don't know."

"As long as Philip is waving an olive branch? And only burning a few Englishmen at the stake now and then?"

William stiffened. "I apologize for trying to save your life." He jerked open the door.

"No, wait!" In two strides Fran blocked his way. "You can't go yet. Not till you hit me on the jaw—or shake hands."

William shook hands. "God bless you, lad. I hope it won't be too long."

The sky was still black when Fran said good-by to Mary and went to the harbor.

Tom Moone stepped out of the shadows. "Boat's waiting for you, sir."

"Tom! What in the name of—"

"The harbor watch on our ships knew something was in the wind when Mr. Hawkins had them moved. We scouted around—and found the *Falcon*." He grinned. "There's ten of us aboard, sir. The rest was too far out in the country to reach."

"But that's impossible! The *Falcon* is provisioned to

keep the sea with the crew that's signed on! She can't sail with ten men who don't belong! She can't—"

"Captain Drake, sir!" Tom reproached him. "You don't think we'd do anything that unseamanlike, sir. We just removed ten of that crew. Everything's in order, sir. Not an extra hand. I swear it!"

The next morning, though, Tom came to Fran's cabin. "Sorry, Captain Drake. One extra hand on board. Here he is, sir. Get along in there, you!" A scuffle, then the door closed.

Fran deliberately let the culprit wait while he read twice through the ship's roster.

Someone whispered, "Sir, I *had* to come!"

Fran's head jerked up. His scalp crawled. A fair-haired boy stared at him with grave eyes. "*Johnny!*"

The boy's wariness vanished in a wide grin. "You know about me, sir? Cousin Mary told you? Sir, I had to come! Cousin Mary is a lovely lady, but I'm not *used* to women."

Fran got up, went to the stern windows and stared out. "You know you've no business on this ship, don't you, Jack?"

"Nobody told me not to come, sir."

"Don't hedge!"

"Yes, sir. I mean, no, sir. You're right. Because even if somebody had told me not to come I'd have tried to do it, sir."

Fran conquered a smile, mustered a frown, and turned. "Think how your Cousin Mary will worry."

"Oh, no, sir! I took care of that. When I heard the men talking at Cousin William's house! I wrote a note. A boy will deliver it to Cousin Mary this morning."

"What if he doesn't deliver it?"

"But he will, sir. He'll get a whole shilling for doing it! I told Cousin Mary where the shilling was. In my box with the dried frog and . . ." His voice trailed off. "And some other things."

Fran looked out the window again. "Jack, I'm going to tell you a secret. Man to man. Just between the two of us. When I was just your age, I did exactly what you've done." He turned, smiling. "We're quite a pair." He held out his arms.

Jack ran to him, burrowing his head against Fran's chest.

"There's only one difference, Jack. The ship I hid on was a coaster, trading up and down the Channel. The *Falcon*—"

"I know, sir. I heard them talking. We may be gone a long time. Where are we going, sir?"

"We'll know that when we open our orders, Jack."

12

Mutiny

Fran opened his orders. Destination, Ireland. Walter, Earl of Essex, was there, putting down a rebellion. The *Falcon* would not anchor in any well-known harbor, but in a certain bay. She could enter it only at high tide. He would wait there until a guide came to take him to Essex. The *Falcon* was provisioned for a month, so there would be no trouble if the guide were delayed.

Just clear of the Channel a northwest gale drove the *Falcon* south, almost within sight of the Spanish coast; the wind came about, and a northeast gale drove her out into the Atlantic.

Seven weeks passed before a starving crew, glassy-eyed with fatigue, stood into the bay. Fran was in the cabin with Jack, dressing to go ashore, when they heard a boat hail the *Falcon*.

Moments later a voice asked, "What have you got aboard this filthy vessel? A pigsty?"

Jack started for the door, fists clenched, lower lip out.

"Jack!" Fran said. "Since when do you leave my presence without being dismissed?"

"I'm sorry, sir!" He stood at attention by the door, his lower lip still flying a storm signal.

They heard Tom Moone explaining, "We've had a rough time of it, sir."

"Come along, Jack," Fran said.

As they reached the deck they heard the stranger's voice again. "That's no excuse. Who's in command of this stink?"

Fran grabbed Jack as he lunged, and held on to him. He spoke to the velvet-clad back and the plumed hat. "Captain Drake is in command!"

The stranger turned. For a moment his slim, haughty face was blank. Then a smile flashed. "Captain Drake! El Draque—the curse of Spain!" He grabbed Fran's hand in both of his. "This is the proudest day of my life! I'm Thomas Doughty, secretary to Sir Christopher Hatton, of the Queen's council. He sent me on a mission to Ireland. And Essex sent me on this errand to escort a certain captain to his presence. But he did not tell me the captain's name, or I'd have—" He smiled down at Jack. "Handsome lad. Your cabin boy?"

"My cousin, Jack Drake."

Doughty held out his hand. "Congratulations, Jack. Do you know you're sailing with the greatest mariner in the world?"

"Better not touch me, sir," Jack said. "I'm pretty dirty,

too, sir. We haven't even had enough water to drink, sir. And salt water is sticky to wash with, sir."

Doughty's smile was rueful. "Jack, I was unforgivably rude. Will you pardon me?"

Jack stared straight ahead. "If my captain commands me to, sir."

"Jack! Mind your manners!"

"Aye, aye, sir. At the command of my captain, sir, I pardon you for being unforgivably rude, sir."

"Spoken like a gentleman and a soldier!" Doughty said.

"I'm not a soldier, sir! I'm a mariner!"

Doughty laughed, slapped Jack's shoulder, and said, "We'll send men and supplies from the guard station to take care of your crew, Captain Drake. Like to go with us, Jack, to see the Earl of Essex?"

"Whatever my captain orders, sir."

"Get ready to go ashore!" Fran said.

"Aye, aye, sir!" Jack marched off.

"Does he like horses?" Doughty asked.

"From what I've heard," Fran said, "he could ride before he could walk."

"Fine! I'll be able to redeem myself."

He commandeered the most spirited steed at the guard station for Jack. "There you are, my lad. How's that?"

"Thank you, sir." And Jack maneuvered so that Fran rode between him and the gentleman with the plumed hat.

Doughty regaled them with stories of London—especially about the furor over Fran's raids in the Caribbean. "I hear Lord Burghley is shaking his head over you, but Sir Christopher Hatton glories in it! One man against the King of Spain! You know, it was a terrific thing! Stupendous! You thinking of going back soon?"

"No," Fran told him. "The element of surprise would be gone. That was the only thing that made it possible. To strike like lightning and then get out."

"I suppose you're right," Doughty said, "but, egad, I wish you were going back! I'd sail with you tomorrow!"

"Sometimes," Jack muttered, "a ship gets pretty foul."

Doughty did not seem to have heard the remark, and Fran decided he would not hear it, either. After all, Jack was only ten, and he was so desperately proud of "his ship."

A keen lad, too, and a worker. In spite of storms that must have scared him half out of his wits, he had learned an amazing lot since they left England. By the time they could go back . . . whenever that was . . .

Jack had grown from a big-eyed ten-year-old to a husky lad of almost fourteen before they saw England again. Fran left him with Mary and hurried to London, wondering why John Hawkins wanted to talk to him.

John's smile was warm and his handclasp firm. "Welcome home, my young hothead."

And Fran, when he tried to speak, found a lump in his throat. Finally he said, "Has the weathercock veered again?"

John pretended to scowl. "I've never said the Queen has a weathercock for a mind. Never! But—if I had, I'd say, 'Yes, the weathercock is about to veer.' Did you hear about what happened at the Scilly Isles?"

Philip, John said, had sent a fleet to seize the Scilly Isles, off Land's End, at the mouth of the Channel. Luckily for England, an epidemic had almost wiped out the Spanish fleet. Otherwise, Philip would have had a naval base at a very handy spot. He could have choked English trade. He could have used it as a steppingstone for an invasion by way of Ireland, Scotland, or the Channel ports.

"Did that waken our sleepers?" Fran asked. "Or do they still think we can keep the peace with Spain?"

"Lord Burghley still talks of peace, but Walsingham is ready to set Spain, Portugal, and England by the ears. He knows war is inevitable. He's ready for some action to bring it on now and get it over with."

"Good for Walsingham!"

"And when it comes to the right man to stir up a hornet's nest . . ." John smiled. "Well, you're to have a talk with Walsingham."

"Thank you!"

"If you handle this right, you may have an audience with the Queen. So—watch your words."

Walsingham was a hawk of a man, thin and dark, with burning eyes. "I understand, Captain Drake, that you have an idea you could strike at the power of Spain?"

"Yes, sir. In the Pacific."

"By what route?"

"Through the Strait of Magellan."

Walsingham spread a chart of the South Atlantic on the table. "A few heads would roll if Philip knew where I got this," he said. "The Spanish really try to guard the secrets of their routes. Now, Captain Drake, if you'll mark your proposed route, your landfalls, your probable time between ports, your—"

"No, thank you!"

"What do you mean?"

"I'll put nothing in writing."

Walsingham stiffened. "You don't trust me?"

"I don't trust fate. I've had a price on my head. I don't intend to put a noose around my neck."

"But you'll want the Queen's backing?"

"And she'll need me if she wants a ship taken through the Strait of Magellan!"

"Just what do you expect me to tell Her Majesty?"

"That I can take the first English ship through the strait!"

"I see." Walsingham stood. "You are with John Hawkins, I believe? If Her Majesty wishes to consider the matter, we'll send for you."

Fran thanked him, bowed, and went to the door. He lingered a moment, but Walsingham did not look up. His hawklike face was cold. Fran thanked him again, and returned to John's house.

"Back so soon!" John said. "What happened?" He listened, and sighed. "The one man of the Queen's council most apt to help you! And you had to—I do wish the years could put a little polish on your tongue!"

"I'll let the courtiers do the talking," Fran said. "When Her Majesty wants action instead of words, I'll be ready!"

"Sometimes," John said, "the path to action is through words, Fran. I'm afraid you've lost your way."

But a few days later Fran knelt in an audience chamber, waiting for the entrance of the Queen. He heard a stir, and the words, "Her Majesty, the Queen!"

Then a crisp voice said, "So you're Captain Drake. The most troublesome subject a monarch ever ruled."

He looked up and stared a moment, bewildered. Why, the Queen was no bigger than Mary! Somehow, he had expected to see a tall, big-boned, deep-voiced woman, towering over everyone. How could anybody so frail-looking . . . One glance into her dark eyes, and he understood. Still kneeling, he bowed his head again. "Almighty God," he prayed silently, "give me life and leave to fight for her!"

The Queen spoke impatiently. "That raid on Nombre. I thought we'd never hear the last of it. In heaven's name, get up, Drake! Sit here!"

And Fran, who could keep his feet in a full gale, stumbled as he took the chair.

"And now you have this mad notion that you can navigate a ship through the Strait of Magellan?"

"Yes, Your Majesty!"

"Even though it's a byword for death and disaster? And the rest of the world has written it off as impossible?"

"With the right sort of ship I can do it, Your Majesty."

"And the right sort of men," she added. "You'd be lucky if your crew didn't mutiny before you entered the strait."

"No crew of mine would ever mutiny, Your Majesty!"

"The invincible Captain Drake! You failed twice at Nombre, didn't you? Once when your men panicked? Then—after a five-months' wait—when a man disobeyed orders?"

Was there anything she did not know? "Yes, Your Majesty," he admitted, "I failed twice."

"Two hopeless failures. Unforgivable failures." She nodded. "Perhaps you *are* the man to conquer the strait. We'll consider the matter, Drake."

"So the Queen is considering the matter?" John Hawkins said. "Prepare to stand by. Why don't we send for Mary and Jack? They'd enjoy the Christmas season in London."

"Christmas! Good Lord, it won't be that long before I'll sail!"

Months later, the spring of 1577, the Queen and her council—with the exception of Burghley—were still discussing plans. Fran listened, said, "Yes, Your Majesty," and "No, Your Majesty," and "That's right, Your Lordships," and kept certain thoughts to himself. He was to sail with five vessels:

The *Pelican,* one hundred tons, for his flagship. (I don't believe the Queen likes the sound of that.) The *Elizabeth,* eighty tons, Captain Winter, gentleman of London, commanding. (Wonder what sort of mariner he is? But the London merchants are helping to raise the money.) The *Marigold,* thirty tons, Captain Thomas commanding. (Now there's a real mariner!) The *Benedict,* a pinnace, Captain Tom Moone commanding. (I'll miss Tom on the *Pelican,* but he deserves his own command.) A new ship, christened the *Swan,* fifty tons, for a supply ship. (One ship named the *Swan* I won't order Tom to sink. We will need her! After we're off soundings, no way to replace a torn sail or a lost anchor!) One hundred and sixty-odd men, including some gentlemen adventurers, under Master Thomas Doughty. (I could do without them. Thank heaven Doughty's in command of them. He's heart and soul back of this! He'll hold them to their purpose!)

Fran had guessed right. The Queen did not think much of the *Pelican* for a flagship. Only one hundred tons! The flagship should be impressive. Why not one of the larger naval vessels? Fran risked arguing the point. He knew he had to. He wanted no high-built *Jesus of Lubecks* on this voyage! The ships must be small and weatherly, he said. Able to tack nimbly in the teeth of head winds.

Then at least the fittings of the *Pelican* must be impressive, the Queen insisted. The captain's cabin, his wardrobe, his dishes . . . Even the mariners should have uniforms to wear on important occasions.

Fran smiled. For the "important occasions" he had in mind, he said, his mariners would be barefoot and stripped to the waist.

A smile touched the Queen's eyes for a moment and faded. "Drake, you're a mariner. No statesman. You'll deal with the Spanish shipping. I'll deal with Spain! In my own way! Do you understand?"

"Yes, Your Majesty."

"So far as the world knows, you'll be going to the Mediterranean, to trade with Alexandria. Even your captains will not know your destination until you are at sea! Your orders will direct you to 'enter the Pacific and try to establish trade with foreign princes.' That's all. Officially, I'll not countenance any action against Spain until the time is ripe." She leaned forward. "And I'll be the sole judge of that time! Do you understand? If your actions at sea threaten my negotiations at home, I'll disown you."

"Yes, Your Majesty. I understand. I know that, when I get back, I might even have to disappear again."

"Disappear? You might be lucky if you had a chance to disappear!"

When the Queen's orders had furnished the *Pelican* with sufficient grandeur, and the Tower had furnished her with guns and ammunition, Fran took her around to Plymouth to complete her outfitting.

Jack beamed at the elegance of the captain's cabin, but scowled at the mention of Doughty's name. "Why do we need *him*?"

"He's in command of the gentlemen soldiers."

"Humph. Think they can stand it when the ships get foul?"

"Jack! Do you want to sail with me?"

"Sir!" His face was blank with astonishment. "Of course!"

"You won't, unless you forget that childish grudge, and mind your manners."

Jack stood, buried in thought, eyes narrowed, lower lip rebellious. "He won't be in command of me, will he, sir?"

"Of course not. But if you're going to hoist that lower lip when we weigh anchor, and—"

"You've taught me not to lie, haven't you, sir?"

"Certainly."

"I promise you, sir, I'll be a gentleman. I'll say 'yes, sir' and 'no, sir' when he speaks to me. I won't talk about him behind his back. But I won't smile at him to his face, either. Because that would be lying. I don't like him, and I don't guess I ever will."

"Jack, I've been a lot of places, and I've known a lot of men. All kinds. Sometimes I've had to judge a man very quickly—know if I could trust him with my life. If

I weren't a pretty good judge of men, I'd be dead."

"Yes, sir. May I go with you, sir?"

"You have nothing else to say about Master Doughty?"

"No, sir. I can't lie to you, sir."

Fran grinned and brushed his fist against Jack's chin. "All right, lad. The subject's closed. Maybe you'll have a chance to grow up before we get back."

Jack heaved a sigh. "I'll grow up before we get started —at the rate things are going!"

"Don't worry," Fran said. "We'll sail by the end of July."

It was mid-December of 1577—and Jack had grown another half inch—before the fleet weighed anchor.

The shivering crew talked of the Mediterranean. Summer in January there, they said. Fran thought of Port St. Julian, just north of the Strait of Magellan. Winter in June there, he knew. Even with luck they couldn't hope to reach Port St. Julian before the middle of April. Could he get through the strait before winter? The passage was less than four hundred miles, but ships had fought the headwinds for three months, only to be forced to give up and turn back. He must get through before winter—or wait through the winter months at Port St. Julian.

"Dear God," he prayed, "let it be *early* April when we reach Port St. Julian!"

"*God willing and the winds with us. . . . If we're windbound, we wait. If we're becalmed, we sit there and rot.*"

That was the story of the next four months. In May the

storm-beaten fleet was off the coast of Brazil, still far north of the strait. Fran knew what he faced. He had lost his race against winter. He would have to wait for spring at Port St. Julian. Wait—while waiting gnawed at his men's hearts.

Tom Moone hailed the *Pelican* and came aboard. "Bad news, Captain Drake. The *Benedict's* not going to make it."

I wish that were the worst of my troubles, Fran thought. He said, "First convenient spot, we'll transfer her cargo, beach her and burn her. Save the iron." He gripped Tom's shoulder. "Be good to have you with me on the *Pelican*."

"Thank you, sir. Sorry to cause this delay."

"Don't worry. The whole crew needs time ashore."

They found a harbor and stood in to fill their water casks. No sooner were they anchored than a northeast gale struck. They clawed off the lee shore and stood out to sea. It was three days before the fleet was together again. The *Swan* was missing. The *Swan*—with tons of supplies they could not do without!

Fran summoned his captains. The *Marigold* and the *Benedict* would search for a place to careen the ships. When they found it, they'd wait there, and light signal fires. The *Elizabeth* and the *Pelican* would search for the *Swan*. "You'll search to the south, Captain Winter, and I'll search to the north."

"But she could not be to the north!" Captain Winter

said. "To sail north, she'd have to sail into the eye of the wind."

"She may be disabled," Fran said.

"Or deserting," Captain Thomas remarked. "Wouldn't be the first ship that deserted a fleet headed for the Strait of Magellan."

"Captain Chester would never desert!" Tom Moone declared.

"There may be a mutiny on board," Fran said. "He may need help."

"If the *Swan's* deserting, and she has a three days' start," Captain Winter said, "there's not much chance to overtake her."

"If she's north and afloat, I'll find her," Fran said. "There's no one aboard her who can outsail me."

Captain Winter smiled. "Or aboard any other ship?"

"Probably not," Fran agreed.

The crew of the *Pelican* did not seem to realize the significance of the search to the north. When the lookout reported the *Swan,* they cheered and fired a signal for her to close with the flagship.

The lookout scrambled down from his perch and spoke in a daze. "She's not coming about, sir! She's going away from us!"

Fran saw the shock of realization wipe faces blank. "Back to your stations!" he ordered. "Her captain needs a little help," he told his men. "We'll overhaul her like she was standing still!"

Another signal from the *Pelican.* The *Swan* continued her flight. She did not stop until the *Pelican* closed with her and sent a warning shot across her bow.

Her captain came aboard the *Pelican.*

"Trouble?" Fran asked.

The captain spread his hands. "Sir, I was only obeying orders."

"Whose orders? You were in charge!"

"But he said the expedition was to be stopped. He said he was equal in command to you, and—"

"Who's equal in command to me?" Fran roared. "*Who?*"

"Master Thomas Doughty, sir."

13

The Golden Hind

When the *Swan* and the *Pelican* turned south, Master Thomas Doughty was in irons, and Fran sat alone in the cabin, staring grimly at nothing. Doughty—the man he had called his friend—the man he had trusted with the truth of their destination! How many others were in the plot? All the gentlemen? Even some of his mariners? Who?

A signal fire guided them to the rendezvous. The other three ships were there, ready for the task of careening. No easy job. Running a ship in as close shore as they dared, lightering all her cargo—a long, backbreaking job. Loading everything into her boats, taking it ashore, lugging it up beyond the reach of the tide. Shoveling out the foul ballast. Then, with their heaviest hawsers secured to the masts, heaving her down, first on one side and then on the other, to burn and scrape away all the barnacles and give her a fresh coat of tar and tallow.

"Beach and burn both the *Benedict* and the *Swan*,"

Fran ordered. "Split up their crews and cargo among the three ships that are going on."

"They'll be heavy laden, sir," Tom Moone said, "with the *Swan's* cargo."

"I hope that's the worst of our troubles," Fran said.

When they had careened and trimmed the ships, the three of them stood to the south—and a roiling unrest sailed with them. On a bleak winter day in June they anchored in Port St. Julian. The first sight that met their eyes was a gibbet, with a heap of bleached bones on the ground.

"Wonder what happened there?" Jack asked.

"The end of a traitor," Fran said.

Master Fletcher, their minister, opened his mouth three times before the words came out. "Captain Drake! You can't mean—you would never—Master Doughty—the secretary to Sir Christopher Hatton! If you condemn him—"

"I'll not condemn him," Fran said. "A jury will hear the charges. They'll find him guilty or not guilty."

"But the gentlemen, sir! If anything happened to Master Doughty, how would they take it?"

"As a warning, I hope."

Master Doughty was very much the soldier when he faced the jury. Yes, he admitted, he had tried to stop the expedition. He had orders from Lord Burghley to stop it.

"That's a lie!" Fran said. "Lord Burghley did not know

our destination! By the express commands of the Queen!"

"He did know," Doughty said, "because I told him."

He refused to accuse anyone else of being in the plan with him. The jury pronounced the sentence. Death. He did not flinch. He only asked that he might take communion before he died.

The night after the execution Fran sat in the tent he shared with Jack, stared at his chart of the strait, and saw Doughty's face, instead.

After a long silence Jack cleared his throat. "I feel bad about it, too, sir. I'd gotten so I kind of liked him."

"You'd better get some sleep, lad."

"Aye, aye, sir." Jack stretched out and closed his eyes. After a while he said, "I wonder how many other traitors there are."

Fran did not answer. He was wondering the same thing.

June shivered to an end. July was more bitterly cold. August began. The unrest that had smoldered began to flare. The gentlemen cursed the mariners, and the mariners snarled at the gentlemen.

Master Fletcher came to Fran. "Captain Drake, I don't know if you're aware of it, but we have a problem on our hands."

"*We,* Master Fletcher?"

"The mood of the gentlemen, Captain Drake. It's very bad. Now, you know and I know that we need the good will of the gentlemen. If the mariners would show more respect—"

"Tell me, Master Fletcher, can the gentlemen take my ships through the strait? Can they hand, reef, and steer? Can they bear a hand when we must make a sudden maneuver?"

"Captain Drake, you're joking! No gentlemen does the work of a common sailor!"

"Then it looks as though I need my mariners, doesn't it, Master Fletcher? As though, on a ship, the mariner is the most important man?" He strode from his tent, beckoned to his drummer, and said, "Summon all hands."

"You'd like me to talk to them?" Master Fletcher offered. "Instill the proper attitude in the—"

"No, thank you, Master Fletcher." When the men had assembled, Fran said, "During the next two days you will all take communion. The third day you will gather here for a sermon. Dismissed."

Master Fletcher rubbed his hands. "An excellent idea, Captain Drake! My sermon will instill the proper attitude in the—"

"I'll preach that day, myself!"

Fran spent most of the next two days in his tent, filling page after page of a blank ledger with his slashing scrawl. The third day, when he faced the men, he opened the book.

"I am not an orator. My training has not given me a gift for fair speaking. But mark what I say to you! For

I've set it down here, and I'll say nothing but what I'll answer for back in England!"

He talked to them of the threat of Spain, of the treatment of English prisoners in the hands of the Inquisition. Of the great undertaking before them—the honor they'd win for their country—and the riches they'd win for themselves.

"Our ships are seaworthy. Our crews must be seaworthy, too! I must have an end to these factions! The men who sail with me must be of one heart! I must have the gentleman to haul with the mariner and the mariner with the gentleman! I would know the man who would refuse to set his hand to a rope! Let him speak now!"

He waited. Silence.

"When we enter the Pacific we shall be three small vessels against the world. Every time we stop to wood and water we may be risking our lives. Every sail we sight will be that of an enemy. If any of you lack courage, speak now. I'll give you the *Marigold,* and you may go home. But see that you do go home! If I find you in my way, I'll sink you! What man wants to go home?"

Again he waited. Silence.

"Then we are of one heart and one purpose. Mariners all! We'll carry England's flag into the Pacific and make Philip pay for the voyage!"

Fran smiled at the cheering, shouting men, then turned to the glum-faced minister. "Well, Master Fletcher, does that seem to take care of our problem?"

Master Fletcher stiffened. "I only hope," he said, "that God's vengeance does not visit this expedition. That we don't all suffer for the crime of one man."

"Since when," Fran asked, "is it a crime to execute a traitor?"

"Captain Drake, you have few enough friends in the Queen's council. And you've made an enemy of one of the few. Sir Christopher Hatton! How do you think he'll feel about the death of his secretary?"

"He'll regret that he trusted a traitor."

"You are a mariner, Captain Drake. No courtier."

"For which I thank God!"

Before they weighed anchor for the strait Fran held a ceremony aboard the *Pelican,* and christened her the *Golden Hind.*

Master Fletcher raised an eyebrow. "That name has nothing to do with Sir Christopher Hatton's coat of arms, of course?"

Fran looked blank. "His coat of arms?"

"A *hind trippant or,* Captain Drake. Should I translate for you? A golden hind."

"Bless me," Fran said. "What a happy accident! I don't know much of heraldry. As you said, I'm no courtier." He smiled blandly until the minister stalked away.

At the entrance to the strait Fran called his captains to the *Golden Hind* for a conference. "I'll lead the way. If I fire two shots, close together, I'm going to heave to for a sounding. If I fire three shots close together, I'm taking a boat ahead to sound."

Captain Thomas smiled and shook his head. "You're a baffling mixture if I may say so, Captain Drake. Sometimes the most cautious mariner who ever sailed. At other times the most reckless—"

"I'm never reckless!"

"Not even when you attempt the Strait of Magellan?"

"What's reckless about it?" Fran asked. "Anywhere any captain has ever sailed a ship I can take another—and make better time!"

Sixteen days later—the shortest passage on record—the fleet reached the Pacific. Cheers echoed from ship to ship. They knelt to thank God for their safe passage.

A gale rose from the northwest, threatening to drive them back into the strait. They fought their way clear and fled to the south, praying that the gale would end before it drove them on a lee shore. For they knew what waited for them if they were driven too far south. Their charts showed it. The strait was the only passage between two continents—to the north, South America—to the south, an ice-locked continent called *Terra Incognita* —Land Unknown.

Day after day for a week Fran wrote in his log: Severe storm. Variable winds.

The fourteenth day he wrote: Storm unabated.

The twenty-first day he wrote: Storm unabated. This day the *Marigold,* Captain Thomas commanding, lost with all hands. No chance to reach her or to save her men.

"Sir?" Jack's eyes were desperate. "How much longer?"

"I don't know, Jack."

"It's driving us south, isn't it, sir?"

"More to the west than to the south now."

"But if it drives us south at *all*, sir, we'll fetch up on a lee shore, won't we? There isn't sea room south of the strait!"

The twenty-third day Fran wrote: Storm unabated. This day we lost contact with the *Elizabeth,* Captain Winters commanding.

"How much longer, sir?" Jack pleaded.

"I don't know, Jack. I've never been through anything like this."

Three days later the storm died. Fran got their latitude. Twenty-six days of the most savage storm any man of them had ever seen, and they had not made good one league to the the north of the strait. In fact, their latitude put them a little to the south of it.

"Due east," Fran ordered.

They sailed east until a lookout reported broken land dead ahead. They anchored offshore and Fran went in a boat to sound for a safe anchorage in a bay between high cliffs.

"Plenty of fresh water and food," he reported. "Thousands of birds. We'll wait here for the *Elizabeth.* Fire a signal gun every hour."

"She may be lost, too, with all hands," Master Fletcher said. " 'Vengeance is mine; I will repay, saith the Lord.' "

All that day and the next there was no answering signal from the *Elizabeth.*

" 'Vengeance is mine.' " Master Fletcher intoned the

words with what seemed to be a sort of gloomy satisfaction.

"We'll stay here two weeks," Fran said. His men needed two weeks ashore, he knew. Maybe longer. A few more days like the last weeks . . . Thank God the storm had ended!

It struck again that night, completely without warning, so suddenly that it snapped their cables and cast them adrift on mountainous waves that thundered against the cliffs around them.

Never had sleeping men hit a deck so fast. Never had Fran given orders faster. "Haul up the mains'l and mizzen . . . helm hard alee . . . let go the bowlines . . . brace about the head yards . . ."

The *Golden Hind* escaped to the open sea. Two sails exploded before they could reef them. Under bare poles she scudded before a wind that drove her relentlessly south.

Time and again they fought to gain an offing to the west. But the sum total of their distance made good, they knew, was to the south—and the lee shore of *Terra Incognita.*

Day after day . . . And the men began to break. Some went mad and had to be tied up. Some huddled in corners and waited for the end.

One week—two—three. The winds subsided. Excepting for the two days of calm, the storm had raged for fifty-two days.

Once more a lookout lay aloft. Some rocky land to

the north of them, he reported. Open water to the south.

Open water? Fran could not believe until he had climbed to the lookout's perch. It was true! No icebound continent blocked the way around the tip of South America!

Tingling with the thrill of his discovery, he called all hands on deck. "This ship and you valiant men will go down in history! We have made the most important discovery of the century! We have un-discovered *Terra Incognita!* We have found an open-water route to the Pacific!"

Mariners and gentlemen yelled themselves hoarse and pounded one another on the back. They promised stout hearts and willing hands for anything that lay ahead. Even when another storm threatened, and they weighed anchor only half-provisioned, with only part of the water casks filled, the men were cheerful.

"Northwest," Fran ordered. His chart showed the coast of South America trending to the west in a great bulge. "Our rendezvous with the *Elizabeth* is in latitude thirty degrees."

Day after day with no sight of land. Where was the western coast of South America? By the time they had reached latitude 40° south, the scant store of water that remained was crawling.

"Due east," Fran ordered. "It seems we have un-discovered the western trend of the coast of South America, too. I don't know why the Spanish are so secretive about their charts. Nobody's going to find anything with them!"

Day after day . . . steady winds . . . no storms . . . The men who had complained of the slimy water were begging for it now. Fran had to post guards over the last water casks—and pray that the guards were dependable.

"Land ho-o-o-o!"

An island. Three Indians with bows and arrows on the beach. Fran went in a boat with presents. The Indians disappeared. He left the presents on the beach, stood off, and waited. After a time the Indians returned without their bows and arrows, carrying meat and woven baskets of other food.

Fran went ashore. "*No español,*" he said. The Indians did not seem to understand. With gestures he explained. The Indians nodded. Yes, water here. The white men could get water. Tomorrow.

Fran did not argue the point. He accepted their gifts, thanked them when they filled the one water cask, and returned to the *Golden Hind.*

The next morning they loaded every boat with water casks and rowed to the island. The three Indians were waiting for them. As the first three white men landed, a hundred savages leaped from the tall reeds. Arrows whistled, killing the men on shore, and wounding every man in the boats.

No water . . . three men dead . . . two dozen others wounded. Hoarding the last slimy dregs in the water cask, they headed toward the mainland. The seriously wounded moaned feverishly. The others began to mutter. The Strait of Magellan would be better than this barren coast! At least they'd have fresh water without dying to get it!

Each time the boats put in to shore—and returned without water—the muttering grew. Even when at last they did find water, it did not blot out the horror of the last days.

"When it's gone—what then?" one muttered.

Jack never complained, but sometimes he stared at Fran long and hard, with questions in his eyes.

"What we need," Fran said, "is the sight of one Spanish ship—and the bigger the better!"

They found her in the harbor of Valparaiso. The *Grand Captain of the South*—evidently one of the biggest ships in the Pacific fleet. Fran studied her, then gave an order that made half his men gasp.

"Stand by to board her!"

14

The raid

As the *Golden Hind* stood in toward the harbor, six men appeared on the deck of the *Grand Captain*. They waved a smiling welcome, and opened a keg of wine.

Tom Moone hit the deck first, yelling, "Get below, dog!" It was one command he knew in Spanish. "*Abajo, perro!*"

With a prize crew on board, they took the *Grand Captain* west, beyond sight of land, removed her cargo and crew, then let her drive.

Plenty of food on the *Golden Hind* now—water, wine, bacon, bread, oil, and vinegar. And some treasure. Two chests of silver and gold. Quite a change in men's spirits that night. They toasted their ship, their captain, their country, and their Queen. They shouted defiance at Philip of Spain.

Jack's slow grin widened. "Their spirits go up and down, don't they, sir?"

"I'll let them work off their high spirits careening the ship," Fran said.

"Again, sir!"

"Again."

Jack heaved a sigh. "Well, at least there's only one ship."

"Yes, only one . . ." Where was the *Elizabeth*? Somewhere to the north of them? Or had she gone down, too, with all hands?

Two months and a dozen prize ships later Fran wrote in his log: 15 Feb. 1579. Latitude 12° 30' S. No sign of the *Elizabeth*. We are nearing Callao, the harbor of Lima.

As they stood in toward Callao, they could see thirty vessels riding at anchor.

"Whew!" Jack said. "Guess no enemy would ever enter that harbor."

"That's probably what they think," Fran said.

And the *Golden Hind* came to anchor in the midst of the Spanish ships. When a voice challenged them and asked what ship they were, one of Fran's prisoners answered for him. She was the *Golden Lady*, a ship of Chile.

Fran gave his orders very exactly, then added, "Remember! Surprise and speed!"

"Aye, aye, sir!"

His men moved so quietly, they overpowered the harbor watches on each vessel so quickly, that no alarm spread from one ship to another.

Only one watchman had the spirit to jeer at Fran. "Search away! You've missed the prize!"

Fran looked crestfallen and let the fellow talk. Men who were bragging sometimes said more than they meant to.

"You're late! Too late! If you loot every ship in Callao, you'll not get half what is on the *Cacafuego!*"

Cacafuego . . . "Spitfire." Probably a nickname for their most heavily armed ship. Fran clutched his head and groaned, "Oh, no! Don't tell me I've missed the *Cacafuego!*"

"But you have! You've missed the greatest prize in the whole Pacific fleet! She sailed two weeks ago for Panama, by way of Paita! With a king's ransom in treasure!"

"Just as well for me that I missed her," Fran said. "She's probably heavily armed."

The watchman swaggered as he bragged of the armament on the *Cacafuego*. Fran sighed, shook his head—and memorized the weight of every gun. He managed to keep on looking depressed until he left the ship.

Back on the *Golden Hind* he snapped orders. "And bear a hand!" he finished. "While the land breeze favors us!"

When the *Golden Hind* weighed anchor, she left confusion behind her. Thirty Spanish vessels, their cables cut, were drifting out to sea.

At dawn Fran looked back on the towering peaks of

the Andes, and said a silent farewell to Callao and all points south. He'd not be that way again soon! By tomorrow the hue and cry would be running up and down the coast. "El Draque! El Draque!"

After prayers he told his men of their quarry—the *Cacafuego*—proudest ship of the Pacific fleet. "She's had a two weeks' start. But I know her tonnage, her cargo, her guns, her sail. We'll overtake her!" He touched the gold chain around his neck. "This to the man who first sights her!"

His confidence swept the crew. They cheered. With every yard of canvas spread the *Golden Hind* sped north. The second morning the wind died. For two days they sat on water quiet as a mill pond. The high spirits of the men died with the breeze. They'd never catch the *Cacafuego* now! They should not have stopped to careen! They should have put into Callao first. They should have—

Once more the breeze filled their sails and lifted their spirits. Once more the *Golden Hind,* under a cloud of canvas, took the bone in her teeth.

Three times they captured a prize, and got word of the *Cacafuego*. Ten days ahead . . . seven days . . . three days . . . They were gaining!

Twelve days out from Callao Fran checked their latitude. The next twenty-four hours would tell the tale. They were getting too close to Panama for safety.

The next day about noon it was Jack who shouted, "Sail

ho-o-o-o! And a big one, sir!"

In half an hour they were near enough to see her plainly. Yes, it was the *Cacafuego,* wallowing along, riding very low in the water.

"We're gaining on her, sir! Fast!"

"Too fast," Fran said. "I don't want to come up with her before night."

"Shall we shorten sail?" one asked.

"No. That would betray our purpose. Break out a dozen empty wine casks. Bend on lines and tow them. That will slow us down."

All afternoon, in spite of her spread of canvas, the *Golden Hind* did not gain on the *Cacafuego.* At evening, when the land breezes sprang up, Fran gave the order, "Cut the tow lines!"

The *Golden Hind* leaped forward as an arrow released from a bow.

The *Cacafuego* came about and hailed them. "What ship?"

Fran measured his distance with a glance, then shouted, "The *Golden Hind,* of Her Majesty, Queen of England! Strike, Don Anton, or I'll send you to the bottom!"

Evidently Don Anton was not impressed. "If you want our colors, come aboard and take them!"

Fran's whistle shrilled; his guns roared. The mizzenmast of the *Cacafuego* fell in a splintering crash. A hail of English arrows over the wreckage prevented any man getting near enough to clear it away.

"The mainmast goes next, Don Anton!"

"Hold your fire! I'll parley with you!"

"I parley with my guns! Strike your colors!"

"Who are you?" Don Anton asked.

The answer was a full-throated roar from the crew of the *Golden Hind*. "El Draque!"

For a moment the men on the *Cacafuego* stood as though frozen. Then they fled below, and Don Anton was alone.

"I have not used my heavy guns," Fran warned him. "One broadside between wind and water, and I'll sink you. I don't want to take the lives of your men."

The *Cacafuego's* colors came down. A prize crew sailed her west. When they were out of the trade route, the *Cacafuego* disgorged her treasure—thirteen chests of gold coins, eighty pounds of gold bars, a chest of jewels, and twenty-six tons of silver.

One of the *Cacafuego's* boys watched the silver going over the side. She was no longer the "Spitfire," he said. She was now the "Spitsilver."

Fran sent all his prisoners to the *Cacafuego*. "Take them to the Governor of Panama," he said. "Tell him not a prisoner has been harmed. Tell him, also, that he'll do well to kill no more English prisoners! El Draque is in the Pacific! Tell him, if he kills another Englishman, I'll hang two thousand Spaniards and send him their heads!"

The grinning crew on the *Golden Hind* watched the *Cacafuego* depart. They slapped backs and shook hands all around. They'd done it! Their voyage was made! They couldn't take the cargo of another *Cacafuego* even if they captured her!

"Sail ho-o-o-o!" came the lookout's cry. "Off our larboard bow. Heading west!"

West? That could mean a ship of the China trade—a ship that would have a chart of the route to the East Indies.

"We'll take her," Fran said. "She might have a few trinkets that don't weigh too much."

Once more a captain refused to strike his colors until his mizzenmast was tangled around his ears. Once more the shout "El Draque!" sent a crew scuttling below.

Yes, she was a ship of the China trade. When Fran let her go, he had a chart of the route to the East Indies. Only . . . how accurate was it? So far, his charts had not been very dependable. The East Indies . . .

"We'd better careen again before we start home, Captain Drake," Tom said.

And how many times before we get home? Fran thought.

Jack groaned. "Careening again! We've spent more time careening her than sailing her!"

Tom grinned. "That's the way of a ship, lad. She spends her first months being put together, and the rest of her life coming apart."

In his cabin Fran wrote: *16 April 1579. This day we weigh anchor from Nicaragua.*

Sixteen months and twenty thousand miles from Plymouth. They had food and water for fifty days. Food for a little longer if they needed to go on short rations. Water would be the problem. It always was.

When they had cleared the harbor he ordered, "Due west, till we find a wind to carry us north."

Heads jerked. Men stared.

"Aye, aye, sir. Due west."

"We've one more mission before we go home," Fran told his crew. "To find the Pacific end of the Northwest Passage. The calculations of our navigators put it in latitude forty degrees north." He returned to his cabin, leaving silence behind him.

West for a hundred leagues—three hundred miles. Still no breeze to carry them north. Instead, they struck the dreaded calms of the doldrums. Day after day motionless, watching for each ripple that promised a hatful of wind. Inching their way, until at last they found a steady wind.

In latitude 38° north they stood in toward the mainland and began the tedious—and dangerous—search. No sign of the passage at 40°—45°—48°. And the land, instead of trending to the east, as the charts had showed, spread out to the west. The Northwest Passage—if it existed—was far longer than their navigators had thought.

They were forty-five days and more than four thousand miles from their last harbor when a gale struck from the north. Fran rationed food and thanked the storm for fresh water.

Tom Moone staggered across the pitching deck to yell in Fran's ear, "A bad leak, sir! We've got to make harbor and *soon!*"

South again, running before the wind. Then, when the storm died, searching along an unknown coast for a safe harbor. One week . . . two . . .

The lookout sighted a bay. Fran went, himself, to sound. They anchored at sunset, but did not risk going ashore that night. The next morning Fran divided the men into three bands—to stand guard, to forage for food and water, and to throw up a fort.

By nightfall they were in their fort, with their bellies full of fresh-roasted meat and good water. For the first time in days their cheerful swagger returned. If any savages showed up—if they were going to have a battle on their hands—at least they'd do it on full stomachs!

They posted guards and slept—only to leap to their feet, grabbing weapons. From the hills came the most hideous wailing, shouting, and moaning they had ever heard. As though five hundred savages were communing with their gods—or their devils. No more sleep that night.

At dawn the savages approached—warriors by the dozens with their bows and arrows—women and children following behind.

"Hold your fire!" Fran ordered. "They may come in friendship."

The Indians brought gifts of food—meat—fish—some kind of dried roots—some hard-baked bread. They laid all their gifts before Fran. Then two men put a crown of feathers on his head. All the Indians knelt as though worshiping him.

Their chief delivered a long harangue. At every sentence he shouted, the kneeling people bowed lower and moaned a response. His gestures said that everything —the presents—the people—the land—belonged to Fran.

Tom Moone grinned. "They think you're a bloomin' god, sir!"

"But they must not!" Fran said. "We've got to make them understand!"

"Going to be hard," Tom declared. "They don't talk any Spanish, and heaven knows we can't talk their jabber!"

When the *Golden Hind* was ready for sea again, Fran took possession of the land in the name of Her Majesty, the Queen of England. He named it "New Albion," because of the white cliffs.

As the crew embarked, the Indians came, weeping and wailing, with a last offering of gifts. As the *Golden Hind* stood out to sea, the moaning wails of the Indians followed her.

Tom Moone chuckled. "They still think you're a god, sir. Well—they could do worse."

Fran glared. "Enough of that, Moone! That's sacrilege! Blasphemy!" He strode to his cabin.

In his log he wrote: 25 July 1579. This day we took our departure from North America, and set a direct course for the Moluccas, in the Pacific.

Once more food and water for fifty days. Once more an unknown sea with nothing to guide him but a chart that might—or might not—be accurate.

The Far East . . . Magellan had died there.

15

Aground

Forty days through the endless, empty ocean. Fran remembered Adam Tanner's words: "What would you do, Drake, if you had been out of sight of land for weeks? . . . That's navigation, Drake!" Yes, he must depend on his navigation now. For he was not following the trade routes on the chart. He was cutting diagonally across them. He could expect no landfall for seven thousand miles. No landfall then, if his charts were wrong or his navigation failed him.

Forty-five days. No sign of land. Short rations now. Fifty days. Nothing but sky and sea. Then the curse of long voyages struck. Scurvy. Day after day the services for the dead, and bodies sliding into the water. Fran was remembering Pedro now: "When you be at sea long as I have, you do it a hundred times."

Fifty-five days . . . sixty . . . sixty-five. Was this to be the end?

On the sixty-eighth day the lookout cried, "Land

ho-o-o!" Once more an alien land and enemy territory. For this was the half of the world where all heathen lands belonged to Portugal.

Fran's men knew the danger they faced in landing, but they were beyond caring. Sounding their way, they stood in toward the shore.

Canoes filled with warriors darted out, surrounding the *Golden Hind*. A shower of arrows hissed through the air.

"Fire over their heads," Fran ordered. "The noise may be enough."

It was. The natives dived overboard and swam away, dragging their canoes after them. The crew of the *Golden Hind* landed, fell on their knees and kissed the ground.

When the sick had recovered, and they had food and water again, they weighed anchor and turned south. Was there somewhere among these islands that they could establish friendship between England and the natives? Somewhere that the people would turn from Portugal to deal with another foreign country? The island of Tidore was supposed to offer rich trade. . . . Fran set his course for Tidore—or for where the island was supposed to be.

Before they reached the might-be location of Tidore, a canoe approached the *Golden Hind*. The man in command hailed them, first in Portuguese, then in Spanish. What ship were they?

His men looked at Fran. What was the safe answer?

Would the word "England" bring friendship, or death?

"The *Golden Hind!*" Fran answered. "Of Her Majesty, Queen of England! Come to establish peaceful trade with the islands!"

The man smiled. The English were welcome! Might he come aboard?

He came, apparently without fear. He was Luis, he said. A half-breed. His blood was both Portuguese and native, but his heart, he declared, was all native!

Where were they bound? Tidore? No, no! The English must not go to Tidore. It was swarming with Portuguese. The English should come to the island of Ternate. There they would be welcome. They would find rich trade. Prince Baber, Sultan of Ternate, would extend the hand of friendship. His father had been treacherously murdered by the Portuguese. He would welcome the English.

"Ternate—much better!" Luis insisted. "You'll come?"

"We'll come," Fran said.

"Good! I shall go ahead to tell of your coming! So the Sultan may be ready for you!" His canoe sped away.

The *Golden Hind,* plagued by contrary winds, followed more slowly. If Prince Baber plotted treachery instead of trade, he was going to have plenty of time to rally his forces.

As they neared the island of Ternate, huge canoes, each manned by four dozen natives, came to meet them. A half-dozen richly dressed young men came aboard the *Golden*

Hind, bringing gifts. The harbor was treacherous, they said. The canoes would tow the *Golden Hind* into port.

With flags and pennons flying, drums beating, trumpets and viols playing, the *Golden Hind* entered the harbor.

When the *Golden Hind* left Ternate, she carried two treasures. The first, a cargo of cloves, weighed six tons. The second, far more priceless, did not weigh anything. It was Baber's promise that he would grant a monopoly of trade in all his islands—and he ruled over more than a hundred—to Her Majesty, Queen of England.

"Next year," Fran promised, "I'll dot these seas with English ships!"

Cheers from the natives when they sailed. Answering cheers from the *Golden Hind.*

Then Tom Moone said, "We'd better find a place to careen."

As usual, Jack groaned. "I hope it doesn't take as long as the last time!"

"Longer probably," Tom said.

Tom was right. They had to set up a smith's forge to hammer out ironwork. When they ran out of charcoal they had to take time to make more. Cutting down trees, sawing them into logs, stacking the logs and setting them afire. Covering them over with earth—just so—that the fire would burn enough, but not too much.

It was December 16, 1579, when Fran wrote: This day we weigh anchor for Plymouth, via the Cape of Good Hope.

He studied his charts. At least seven thousand miles to the cape—in a direct line. But first they must find their way through these islands. Islands that stretched—as nearly as he could guess—for about three thousand miles along the equator. If they could find a passage around them to the north . . .

For three weeks they beat their way north, seeking an open passage, only to find, time and again, that what looked like open water was not.

They searched to the south. At last, open water and a fair wind! They cheered, spread every yard of canvas, and roared along. They struck without warning, and the shock knocked most of the men flat. The press of wind drove the bow of the ship hard into whatever they had struck.

"Sound the bilges!" was Fran's first command.

They were taking some water, Tom reported, but no sign that the hull had been stove in. He thought it was safe to warp her off.

"Stern anchors!"

But the anchors plunged down and down, and the cables ran out to the end. They sounded with their dipsey lead. It plunged down and down, too. No bottom! How could a ship be aground at the bow when there was no bottom at her stern? What reef or rock could rise from the ocean floor in a miles-high column, and give no warning of its presence?

"Read the prayers, Master Fletcher," Fran said. "Only God's mercy can save us now."

Master Fletcher read the prayers. He also preached a sermon. All was lost! They would perish here! This was the fate that had hung over them since Port St. Julian! All for the sins of one man! All because—

Fran interrupted. "That's enough, Master Fletcher. Go below. I'll deal with you later."

The minister went below, still talking.

"We'll jettison enough cargo to float her," Fran said.

Eight of their heaviest guns went first. Then three tons of their cloves. The ship did not stir.

"Start handing up the silver," Fran said.

The men groaned. Were they going to have their two-year struggle for nothing?

"The most precious treasure we carry doesn't weigh an

ounce," Fran told them. "It's our treaty with Baber. If we get home with nothing but that, our voyage is still made! Break out the silver! Bear a hand!" He went to the bow to check again. "No . . . stop."

It was no use to hope they could float her off. The ebbing tide had left her fast in a cleft of rock, with only six feet of water at her bow. She drew thirteen feet.

Fran knelt with his men and commended them to the care of the Almighty. God, who had brought them through so many dangers, God, whose hand could still the raging sea, would sustain them now. All night Fran moved from man to man. Over and over he said, "We must believe. We must pray."

At dawn the wind shifted. The *Golden Hind* listed, stirred, grated upon the rocks, and plunged stern-foremost. She wallowed, lurched, and righted herself.

Fran read a prayer of thanksgiving, then went to his cabin. He returned presently with a placard. "My compliments to Master Fletcher. I'll see him now."

All that day Master Fletcher had to stand by the mainmast, wearing the placard:

FRANCIS FLETCHER

THE FALSEST KNAVE THAT LIVETH

"I'll have no more sermons," Fran told him, "from a man who has lost his faith in the Almighty! Hereafter, I'll read the prayers!"

In September of 1580, almost three years since she had sailed, the *Golden Hind* entered the English Channel. Fran hailed a fishing boat and asked one question: What of the Queen?

He could feel his men holding their breath as they waited for the answer. If Her Majesty had died, and another ruler were on the throne of England . . .

The Queen was alive and well, the fisherman told them. Cheers echoed over the ship. If all was well with the Queen of England, then all was well with the *Golden Hind!*

It might not be that simple, Fran knew, but he didn't go into what he was thinking.

Jack grinned down at him. Jack was almost eighteen now, and over six feet tall. "Wonder where you'll go next, sir?"

"Back to the Spice Islands!"

"May I go with you, sir?"

"If I said 'no,' they'd probably roust you out of the hold as soon as we were off soundings, wouldn't they?"

"Yes, sir!" Jack admitted cheerfully. "Any time you sail anywhere, you'll find me on your ship!"

"I've a better future than that for you," Fran said.

"There *is* no better future than to sail with you, sir."

"What if I told you that the next time you sail you'll be in command of your own ship?"

Jack's eyes glowed. "Captain John Drake!" he whispered. "In command of his own ship!"

A pain stabbed through Fran's chest. The years had not eased the ache over Johnny's death.

"I know what I'll call my ship!" Jack said. "The *Francis!*"

"Thank you, lad. One thing, Jack—when we get home —and Mary asks all about the voyage—"

"Yes, sir!" Jack chuckled. "Won't we have some exciting things to tell her! About the storm when we lost our anchors, and about going aground in the Spice Islands, and—"

"That"s just the sort of thing we won't tell her!"

"We won't?"

"Do you want her to be scared to death the next time we sail to the East Indies?"

"Oh . . . But when she asks what was the most interesting thing in the last three years . . ."

"Describe a sunset!"

"You're joking, aren't you, sir? No . . . you're not. Sir, doesn't a man ever tell a woman the truth?"

"Not about the sea!"

There must have been lookouts posted at Plymouth, watching for their ship. As they entered the harbor, cheering crowds thronged the headlands. But just one boat put off to meet them, bringing Mary and the Mayor of Plymouth. Fran could see baggage for Mary in the boat. What was in the wind?

Mary came aboard, laughing through her tears. "Oh,

Fran! Thank God you're safe!"

The Mayor wore an anxious frown. "Captain Drake, may we talk in your cabin?"

Fran gave Jack a glance that said, "Watch your tongue!" and turned Mary over to him. "This way, sir." When they were in his cabin, "Trouble again?"

Very serious trouble, the Mayor said. Philip of Spain had more power than ever. Sebastian, King of Portugal, was dead. Last of his line. Two men had laid claim to the empty throne. A certain Don Antonio of Portugal, and Philip of Spain. Philip had won the argument. Had defeated Don Antonio's forces and seized the throne.

"You can see what that means," the Mayor said.

Yes, Fran could see. Once Philip had claimed all heathen lands in half the world. Now he could claim all heathen lands in all the world. And—what was more serious—he could back up his claim with Portugal's fleet. "About time I was getting home!" Fran said.

"Captain Drake, you could not have come back at a worse time. Things have been in a turmoil about you ever since Captain Winter reported you were in the Pacific."

"Winter? You mean the *Elizabeth* came home?"

"A year ago. Captain Winter said he reached the strait again, after a severe storm, thought that you had gone down, so—"

"Why, that lily-livered knave! I'll have his head for—"

"You'll be lucky to keep your own head, Captain Drake.

Philip of Spain has handed down an ultimatum: Your head—or war."

"I'm to be banished again?"

"For the moment you'll hide your ship behind St. Nicholas's Island, and—ah—await developments."

"My cargo?"

"Mr. Tremayne will be sent to seal it. I know we can trust you not to disturb it in the meantime."

"Thank you so much!"

The Mayor flushed. "I'm only carrying out orders, Captain Drake. We'll send supplies to the *Golden Hind* —at night. You'll want to be careful, though, about who boards your ship. We should have a watchword."

"How about 'Hail, Philip of Spain!'?" Fran growled. "And the answer could be 'Let all Englishmen kneel!' . . . I'm sorry," he said quickly. "The challenge shall be, 'God save the Queen!' and the answer, 'Long to reign over us!' "

"Thank you, Captain Drake. I—I hope everything works out—some way." He did not sound as though he had much hope. They returned to the deck.

Jack was saying to Mary, "You know one of the things I'll remember longest? Sunset on the snows of the Andes!"

Fran summoned all hands and explained the situation. "I cannot land," he said. "The *Golden Hind* must disappear. But you men would be safe ashore, if you scattered and did not talk. I can ask for a fresh crew, and—"

What an uproar! A strange crew on the *Golden Hind*? Just let them try! There'd be a few skulls cracked!

"I've heard legends about you, Captain Drake," the Mayor said. "I'm beginning to believe they are true. Mrs. Drake may stay with you until—ah—I'll tell them to hand up her baggage."

Mary was no longer smiling. "I thought we were sailing to London?"

"Ah—not just yet," the Mayor said. "But you'll be with Captain Drake until—ah—Her Majesty—ah—comes to a decision. Until she—ah— Good luck, sir!" He returned to his boat.

Fran smiled at Mary. "We'll have a long visit." He took one last look at the town and the cheering people. "Up anchor!"

A boat came that night to their hideout at St. Nicholas's Island, bringing supplies, Mr. Tremayne, and William Hawkins.

Mr. Tremayne sealed the cargo. He, too, said he hoped things would work out—some way.

William tried to cover his anxiety with congratulations, but he could not fool Mary.

"Please tell me!" she begged. "Why must Fran hide?"

"Because Philip says, 'Deliver that pirate to me, or there will be war.' "

"But Fran isn't a pirate! He's never fought the way a pirate does!"

"I know, Mary. He's 'just a man who's at war with the King of Spain.' But he's a little before his time, Mary."

"What will happen?"

William couldn't answer that. He, too, could only hope that things would work out.

John Hawkins came, bringing news from London. Yes, things were in quite a turmoil, he admitted.

Fran noticed how pale and worn John was. He had aged ten years in the last three. "You look as though you've been through a battle, yourself," he said.

"I have," John said. "For over two years. My father-in-law is dead. I've taken over his work."

"Treasurer of the navy? You?"

"Yes."

"You've given up the sea?"

"I'll do anything to save England! Fran, we must have more ships! Someone must make a hundred pounds do the work of a thousand. Someone must stop the thievery that was going on. Poor Father Gonson. Before he died, he said, 'I pluck a thorn out of my foot and put it in yours.' I didn't think it would be that bad. I thought he was old and tired and heartbroken. Now—I feel old and tired and heartbroken, too. I'm facing a harder fight than I ever faced at sea. But I'm still fighting! Trying to build up our fleet. Trying to change old ideas. Trying to make men understand that we need handy, weatherly vessels, heavily gunned, to—"

"Good for you! But I wouldn't have your job if they gave me the navy."

John smiled wearily. "Just as well. You wouldn't last a week."

"You build them, and I'll fight with them!" Fran said. Then he added. "If they'll let me fight! Oh, if they'd let me go to London and talk to the Queen, I could—"

"You'd be safer out of the country," John said. "I hope —for your sake—that you're ordered to disappear."

Mr. Tremayne came again in the night—this time with orders from the Queen. Captain Drake was to report to London with "some of the curiosities" he had brought back.

And then what? Fran wondered. The Queen had made it plain enough before he sailed: "If your actions at sea threaten my negotiations at home, I'll disown you. . . . Disappear? You may be lucky if you have a chance to disappear!"

16

The King of Spain demands a head

"I'll see Mrs. Drake safely home," Mr. Tremayne said, "and young Jack."

"Hmmm . . ." Fran studied a moment. So far, Jack had not told Mary any of the "more interesting" adventures of the *Golden Hind*. But if he were alone with Mary for a week or two or three . . . "I think I'll take Jack to London with me."

Jack beamed at the news. "Maybe I'll get to see the Queen!"

He thinks it's all smooth sailing now, Fran told himself. Well—whatever was in store for him—surely Jack would be safe. "Yes, lad," he promised, "I'll ask to present you to Her Majesty, and I'll see that you're decked for the occasion."

A week later Jack, resplendent in silk hose, satin trousers, and a gold-embroidered velvet coat, knelt before the Queen.

Her Majesty was gracious. "So you've spent almost

seven years at sea with Captain Drake? You should be a master mariner by now. We must remember you."

Jack's audience was over. A few moments of time—a few words from the Queen—but he went out with a face shining brighter than his new finery. Fran knew how he felt.

Then the Queen was abrupt. "We've a crowded calendar, Captain Drake. You may have half an hour to explain yourself!"

At the end of half an hour she sent orders: Cancel all appointments for the morning. At the end of three hours she sent orders: Cancel all appointments for the afternoon.

At the end of six hours she said, "The first English ship through the Strait of Magellan. The first English ship to challenge Philip in the Pacific. The first English ship around the world. The first commander of any nation to sail his ship around the world and live to get home again. You've made the greatest discovery of our time—the open-water route to the Pacific. You've taken possession of a vast dominion for England. You've opened our trade with the East Indies. Zounds! All my other captains put together have not matched your deeds! And now—what in heaven's name am I going to do with you?"

"Let me follow up what I have begun, Your Majesty! Send me back to the East Indies! The monopoly of trade is ours for the taking! But we must strike now while the time is ripe!"

For a long time the Queen was silent. At last she shook her head. "You're a mariner, Drake. No statesman. I must have time to think. You'll remain in London. At a convenient place."

"We could stay with my cousin, John Hawkins."

"You must be in a safer place than that!" she said harshly. "Don't you realize your life is in danger?"

Jack strutted about their apartment, where they had liveried men to wait on them—and uniformed guards at the door. "We're living like princes!"

And prisoners, Fran thought. His next quarters might be the Tower. Or was he important enough to be a prisoner in the Tower? He shrugged off the thought. "Shall we work on navigation?" he asked.

"Fine!" Jack chuckled. "I remember when I was thirteen. I'd been with you three years. I thought I knew all there was to know. But there's so much to learn!"

"*So much to learn. So little time.*" Fran did not realize he had said it aloud until he saw Jack's puzzled look. "We may sail for the Spice Islands soon," he said.

Every day—and sometimes many times in one day—the Queen sent for him. Every day he repeated his belief: The only defense against Philip was attack. So Philip had wrested the throne of Portugal from Don Antonio? Why not go to Don Antonio's aid and set him on Portugal's throne? The price of their help—a fortified base in the Azores. That was the landfall of all the returning treasure fleets. A very handy spot for England to hold! With a base in the Azores, and the trade with the East Indies . . .

After a month Her Majesty still needed time to think. Captain Drake could return to Plymouth—and await orders.

"She treated us like princes!" Jack told Mary. "Servants to wait on us! Guards at the door!"

"Is everything . . . settled?" Mary asked.

"Not quite," Fran said.

"What do you do now?"

"Wait."

"She'll send for us again!" Jack was confident. "The next time will be even more exciting!"

Fran saw Mary shiver. "You mustn't worry," he told her when they were alone.

But she did. Hoofbeats in the night, and she trembled. A knock on the door, and she gasped.

One night they heard a measured rap and Mr. Tremayne's voice, sounding very formal for the voice of a friend. "Captain Drake? A message from the Queen."

Fran opened the door, and saw the uniformed men behind Mr. Tremayne. This was it.

"Captain Drake, I have been directed to make an accounting of the treasure on the *Golden Hind,* to remove it, and send it to the Tower. The *Golden Hind* will then be sent around to London. You will please accompany me to the ship."

"Shall I be ready to take her to London?"

"No, Captain Drake."

"Then I'll not be long." He smiled as he kissed Mary. "I'll be back soon, dear."

He knew that she didn't believe him. He picked up his cape and hat, and marched off, flanked by the guards.

Mr. Tremayne said nothing until the two of them were alone in Fran's cabin. Then he smiled. "You are to be left alone with the treasure before I begin my audit. Walsingham has suggested that a trifling amount for you —say ten thousand pounds—would not be missed. And another trifling amount to pay off your crew. They'll be discharged when they reach London." His smile widened. He chuckled, slapped Fran's shoulder, and went out.

Fran returned home, still under guard, with his "trifling amount," and continued to wait.

It was late in March—almost seven months since he had brought the *Golden Hind* into harbor—when another summons came from the Queen. The *Golden Hind* was at Deptford. Captain Drake, and any of his crew who were ashore, would report to the ship for a ceremony.

"Hmmm . . ." Tom Moone said. "Wonder if she's going to turn the whole lot of us over to Philip?"

"If you want to sign on the first vessel sailing to foreign ports, I won't stop you," Fran said.

"Where you go, we'll go along," Tom declared. "Been with you so long now, be hard to break the habit."

They spent two days in Deptford, getting the *Golden Hind* cleaned, polished, and decorated for the ceremony —whatever it was to be. The Queen came aboard in state, with lords and ladies, foreign envoys, and stern-faced guards.

Fran obeyed the command and knelt before her.

"The King of Spain has demanded thy head of me," she said, "and here I have a golden sword to cut it off."

There was a pause. Fran waited. Then he felt a tap on his shoulder, and heard the French envoy say, "Arise, Sir Francis Drake!"

In the fierce joy of the moment Fran had a wild desire to laugh. So Her Majesty "had a weathercock for a mind," did she? What a statesman! She had not only spurned Philip of Spain's ultimatum, but she had made France a party to her defiance! She was ready for action now! He'd be sailing to the Spice Islands before . . .

But the Queen showered him with honors and riches—and still needed time to think.

Mary came to London and was breathless with the wonder of it all. Riding in their own coach and four. People lining the streets and roads, shouting for their hero.

Mothers holding up their babies. "Look at him, dearie! Look! You'll not see his like again!"

People bringing the sick to him, as though he had the gift of the king's touch, and could cure disease.

Affairs of state, with gentlemen bowing over Mary's hand. "Lady Drake, this is an honor!"

Then one night at a ball a beautiful young woman, Elizabeth Sydenham, curtsied before Mary. "Lady Drake,

I've looked forward so much to meeting you!" As the music stopped her voice carried through the crowd. "It must be so exciting—being married to a pirate!"

It was Mary who broke the shocked silence. "He isn't a pirate, dear."

"No?" Elizabeth was plainly disappointed. "Practically everybody I know calls him a pirate."

"He's never been a pirate," Mary said gently. "He's a man who's at war with the King of Spain. That's all. I'm sorry to disappoint you."

"Thank you, Lady Drake." Elizabeth sighed. "It did sound so exciting."

The crowd recovered and laughed indulgently. Mary was still smiling—with her lips.

But that night when she was alone with Fran she said, "I'll be glad when we can go home to Devon."

"The first minute it's possible," he promised.

When the day came they left Jack in London—he was sailing around to Plymouth in one of the Hawkins ships—and started overland in the coach and four.

Their journey through the countryside was as slow as one of the Queen's progresses. Cheering throngs blocking the road in every village. Invitations to visit at dozens of stately homes.

In Devon, Fran said, "We'll make one more stop. I want you to see Sir Richard Grenville's place—Buckland Abbey."

"He'll be there?"

"No, I think he's sold it, but the servants will show it to us, I'm sure."

A footman opened the door. "Sir Francis! Lady Drake! Welcome to Buckland Abbey! May I—"

"Nothing at the moment," Fran said. "We'd just like to look around. I'll ring if I want you."

"Yes, Sir Francis." He ushered them into the Great Hall, and left them.

"He's very friendly, isn't he?" Mary said. "Letting us look around alone." She smiled. "I can't get used to being called 'Lady Drake.' "

They toured a part of the mansion house, looking into dozens of rooms. They went outside and strolled in the edge of the deer park. They saw one of the barns—over a hundred and eighty feet long. They saw the orchards, and the fields, stretching away into the distance.

"A tenant is farming three hundred acres now," Fran said, "but quite a bit of the land is lying fallow."

"How big *is* this place?" Mary asked.

"I'm not sure," Fran said. "Should we take a week and try to see it all?"

"Perhaps some day we'll come back," Mary suggested. "Shall we go home now?"

"We are home." He chuckled and hugged her. "Buckland Abbey is ours. Remember, Mary? I promised you that some day I'd buy you a farm in Devon?"

"Fran! Oh, Fran!" Her face was against his coat.

"Mary! You're crying! I thought you'd like it!"

"You still don't know much about women, do you? I'm crying because I'm happy. I didn't think you'd ever forget the sea and be content to—" Then, without looking up, she read his thoughts. "And you haven't, have you? You'll never forget the sea. When do you sail again?"

"The next voyage will be just a trading expedition," he said. "To the East Indies."

"Will you take any of the Queen's ships?"

"Of course."

"Then it isn't just a trading expedition, is it?"

"You don't understand about our navy, dear. We can't afford a fleet that does nothing but fight. When the Queen's ships aren't needed for defense, Her Majesty often sends them on trading expeditions. Lets them earn their tar and tallow. You see?"

"Will Jack go with you?"

"In command of his own ship! He's going to name her the *Francis*."

She looked at the walls of the mansion house. "It will seem very big when I'm alone."

"You'll not be alone," Fran said. "You'll have all the servants. And you can give balls and dinners—all sorts of things."

"Yes, dear."

"Mary, I've got to go. I was the one that opened the trade with the East Indies. You see that, don't you?"

"Yes, Fran. After all, I did marry a sailor, didn't I? No tears when you sail for the East Indies! That's a promise!"

None that I'll see, he thought. But I've got to go!

The Queen—after more months of thinking about it—refused to let Fran command the expedition to the East Indies. There was too much danger of war. He might be needed in England.

When four ships weighed anchor from Plymouth, Fran stood on shore with Mary, waving to Jack on the *Francis*.

Mary tucked her hand in Fran's. "Poor darling. You look like a lost dog!"

"I'll be all right," he said. For two days he roamed the grounds of Buckland Abbey. "How'd you like to give a feast?" he suggested. "Invite the whole countryside?"

"We could, dear," Mary said, "but it wouldn't help."

"What do you mean?"

"I know. Any house—no matter how big or how small—can have a great emptiness. And people—just people—can't fill it. Fran, dear, I'm sorry, for your sake, that you couldn't go. This is the first time you've been left behind."

"So this is what it's like. You know, Mary, I've always thought I had courage. Compared to you, I'm a coward."

"Francis Drake!" He hadn't seen her eyes blaze that way for years. Not since the day he told her he'd been accused of deserting the *Minion*. "Nobody living can call you a coward! Not even you! You're *not* a coward! You're just— Well, men aren't *supposed* to be left behind! . . . Go on and laugh!" She was fighting a losing battle against a smile, herself. She turned away. "Go on and laugh!"

"I shall! I'll laugh every time I think of it!"

A few months later he remembered it with an ache in his throat. For Mary was dead.

Buckland Abbey was unbearable now. He closed it and went to one of the houses he'd bought in Plymouth. That didn't help. Mary had been right. Any place, big or little, could have a great emptiness.

William Hawkins was with him when a dispatch came from London. A Royal Commission was to investigate the state of the navy. Sir Francis Drake was to serve as an adviser to the commission.

Fran crushed the paper and hurled it to the floor. "I'll be hanged if I'll go! What a way to run a country! Send an incompetent like Fenton to command the expedition to the Spice Islands—and ask me to sit as an 'adviser' on the state of the navy!"

"I hope you do go," William said. "John needs you. You know what people are accusing him of? Dishonesty. Skimping his work—using poor material—and pocketing the difference."

"Why, those dastards! I'll have their heads!"

Fran was in the midst of a discussion with the Royal Commission when a Mr. Chessley sent for him. A matter of greatest importance, the message said. Mr. Chessley was one of the heaviest investors in the expedition to the Spice Islands. Fran excused himself and went.

Three other merchant-investors were with Mr. Chessley. They nodded abruptly and sat scowling while Mr. Chessley gave Fran the news. The expedition had returned. A complete failure. In the South Atlantic, some Spanish ships had challenged them. They had turned back. Then a storm had scattered the fleet. The *Francis* had disappeared with all hands.

17

Olive branches and daggers

Jack's ship missing with all hands! Fran stared unheeding at the frowning merchants. Gradually what Mr. Chessley was saying penetrated. The merchants, it seemed, were very angry about the whole affair. Sir Francis Drake had promised them immense profits with his harebrained scheme of an expedition to the East Indies. Instead, they had suffered heavy losses.

Fran jumped to his feet. "The next time you send a fleet to trade with the Spice Islands, put a mariner in charge! And don't tie his hands with idiotic orders about 'getting along with Spain'!"

Mr. Chessley's moon face turned red under his shock of white hair. He and the other merchant-investors had engaged in profitable trade for—

"Trade?" Fran snorted. "You call your two-for-a-shilling operations 'trade'? When we open trade with the East Indies, you'll see profits you never dreamed of!"

Mr. Chessley stiffened. He and his friends had been

merchants—successful merchants—when Sir Francis Drake was nothing but a prentice on a coaster. And they would continue to be successful merchants, without having trouble with Spain!

"Then sit at home and count your guineas!" Fran suggested. "When Philip decides to invade England, he'll appreciate your nice fat moneybags!"

He slammed out of the meeting and went back to growl at the Royal Commission investigating the state of the navy.

That night, when his anger had left him, there was nothing but an aching emptiness. Where was Jack? Had his ship gone down? Or had she gone aground on a lee shore? Had the men escaped? If they had reached shore —then what? Were they in enemy hands? How long would he have to live without knowing? With hope and despair gnawing at him?

This, too, he thought, was what Mary had had the courage to face. Months and years of waiting, wondering, hoping and praying.

Excepting for John Hawkins' brief words of sympathy, nobody mentioned Jack. Plenty of talk about the expedition. Grim or joking, wry or bitter, men spoke of the "harebrained scheme."

And the days and nights creaked by. Days of work he hated. Nights he hated, too. Court functions, dinners, and balls he must attend. Facing sly jibes, one-sided smiles, and silences that said more than words. Sometimes when he entered a crowded room he muttered, "I'd rather navigate the reefs of the Spice Islands again!"

One night a young lord taunted him. "After all, Sir Francis, you've never defied the real power of Philip, have you? You've merely skulked about in his far-off possessions, seizing ships that weren't armed for such action."

"When the time comes," Fran growled, "I'll strike him nearer home! I'll strike so close home I'll singe his beard!"

The young man lifted a languid eyebrow. "Dear, dear! Your modesty overcomes me."

"What the devil have I got to be modest about?" And Fran strode out, leaving a buzzing behind him, and went back to his room at the inn.

A letter propped on a shelf waited for him. He caught a glimpse of his scowling face as he picked it up. "You'd do to scare children with," he muttered. He ripped open the letter. No signature. It must be poisonous. What was there left to say to him that he hadn't heard? Well, he was getting used to it, and there was nobody else they could hurt. He read:

Dear Sir Francis Drake

I'll not sign this, because my name would mean nothing to you. I'm just one of the thousands of people who are sympathizing with you in your sorrow—losing first your wife, and then your cousin.

Lady Drake was a very kind and gracious lady. Captain John Drake was a very gallant gentleman.

I know you pray every night that his ship may get back. This waiting must be very hard. Hope and despair mixed up together must be worse than knowing.

May God comfort you and bless you. And may God take care of you. England needs you, Sir Francis Drake.

After a time Fran looked at his reflection again. "Mark this down and remember it, Drake! It's a command! Get that scowl off your face and keep it off!"

Many times in the next year he had to remind himself of that command. Each time the Queen ordered him to assemble a fleet—to stand by—to dismiss it—to assemble—to stand by—to dismiss—to assemble . . .

A fleet to aid Don Antonio—a fleet to seize the Azores—a fleet to go to the Spice Islands—

But each time the Queen finally changed her mind and said, "You're a mariner, Sir Francis. No statesman!"

And he said, "Yes, Your Majesty," without scowling.

Back and forth from London to Plymouth. Back and forth from dockyards and harbors to balls and dinners. And the long wait gnawing at him. Sometimes at a ball he left the crowded rooms and went outside to look up at the stars and wonder how much longer.

He was on a terrace one night, with the music of the dance behind him and the stars above him, when he heard the sharp report of a slap, and a girl's angry voice.

"He's no pirate, you white-livered stay-at-home!"

And a girl dashed out onto the terrace and ran headlong into him. He caught her to keep her from falling.

"I beg your—" She looked up. Tears in her eyes. Angry tears, without a doubt. It was quite the stormiest—and most beautiful—face he had ever seen. Slim, with dark eyes and black hair. She gasped. "Oh! Sir Francis! Let me go, please!"

"I can't risk it," he said. "Not till you dry your tears. You're a menace, dashing about that way. The next man you run into might not have his sea legs." He gave her his handkerchief.

"Thank you. You don't remember me, do you? I'm glad. I hope you never do."

"I never saw you before," he declared. "I couldn't possibly have forgotten . . . I have it! You're related to little Elizabeth Sydenham. The girl who thought it would be so exciting to be married to a pirate."

"That was most thoughtless, cruel thing anybody ever said."

"Oh, come now! She was only repeating what she had heard. You can't expect a child—"

"She was no child! She was eighteen! What were *you* doing when you were eighteen, Sir Francis?"

"But that's different," Fran said. "Boys grow up faster than girls. At eighteen I had survived eight years on a Channel coaster. I doubt if Elizabeth Sydenham could have dressed herself without the help of two maids when she was—"

"I never needed more than one maid!" she stormed.

"And if you had to wear what we have to wear—"

"You're not Elizabeth! You couldn't be!"

"Of course not, Sir Francis. Girls never grow up, do they?"

Elizabeth Sydenham. Eighteen in '81. Not quite twenty-two now . . .

He bowed and offered his arm. "I'm sure your escort is looking for you."

"I doubt it," she said. "I slapped his face."

"Then he's looking for you harder than ever."

As they returned to the dance, a handsome young man hurried through the crowd. "Elizabeth! Where have you been?"

"I'm dancing this next figure with Sir Francis."

Fran bowed. "She thinks pirates are exciting."

When the ball ended, he and Elizabeth were back on the terrace, talking about the stars.

A month later, as Fran dressed for the evening, he stopped to glare at his reflection. "Mark this down and remember it, Drake! You're too old for her! If you've half the sense you think you have, you'll not go to that ball tonight. . . . At least you'll not walk in the garden with her."

Two hours later he stood in a garden with Elizabeth, looking up at the stars. "Jack and I watched them around the world," he said. "I wish you could have known Jack."

"I met him, Sir Francis. He was a gallant gentleman."

A gallant gentleman. How many times had he read those words in the letter?

"This last year must have been very hard for you, Sir Francis. Hope and despair mixed up together must be worse than knowing."

Elizabeth! She had written the letter!

"Yes, it was hard," he said. "For a while I was very bitter. Frankly, I wasn't fit to live with. Then someone wrote me a letter. She didn't sign it. But I've always hoped that some day I'd find her. You know what I'll do when I do find her? I'll propose to her."

"*What!*"

"I love her."

"That's the most fantastic— You can't fall in love with someone you don't know."

"But I do know her. Through her letter. I think I know her better than people who see her every day and call her by name. So, when I find her, I'll propose to her." He held out his hands. "Will you wish me luck?"

"You're completely mad," she said, "but I wish you luck." She laid her hands on his.

He gripped her fingers and stared over her head. "Dear Elizabeth," he said, "this is my answer to your letter. Thank you."

She caught her breath. "How did you guess?"

He still did not risk looking at her. "Dear Elizabeth, let me finish my answer, please. I loved you for your letter before I knew your name. And I've loved you for yourself before I knew you wrote the letter. Dear Elizabeth, please tell me this: Do you still think it would be exciting to be married to a pirate?"

"No!"

He released her hands and bowed. "You don't stand off and on about things, do you?"

"No, I don't! And if you *ever* say 'pirate' again," she declared, "I'll divorce you!" Then she was in his arms.

"Elizabeth! I didn't—I thought you didn't—"

"Serves you right!" she said. "That was the stiffest proposal I *ever* had!"

They laughed together.

Then she said, "I love to hear you laugh. I hope you'll always find things to laugh about. Even if sometimes you're laughing at me. And I hope . . ." She stopped.

"Yes, dear?"

"It isn't any use to hope that. I sha'n't tell you."

"You're hoping there'll never be war with Spain?"

"I said I wouldn't tell you, and I sha'n't! Ever!" Then she added, "The Queen has kept the peace for almost thirty years, hasn't she?"

"Some call it peace. Because Philip is waving an olive branch, and they don't see the dagger up his sleeve."

"You think—"

"I'd like to be married while he's still waving olive branches."

"Next April?" she suggested. "Most people I know are married in April."

"Before that," he said. "By April the olive branches may not be in season."

They were married in February. The next April the olive branches still seemed to be "in season." In fact, Philip was waving more olive branches than usual.

Crops had failed in two of his provinces. Famine threatened his people. He needed corn—the corn of every country. Wheat from England—oats from Scotland—all the corn he could get. For once English ships could come and go in his harbors. English mariners would be safe. English merchants could make a handsome profit.

The good news spread through England. Trains of pack horses wallowed through the spring mud, bringing grain to the port towns. Captains chartered extra ships. Sailors sang as they worked. The townspeople cheered as each corn ship sailed.

Mr. Chessley of London was in Plymouth and came to call at Buckland Abbey. "Well, Sir Francis! Peace at last, eh? I always knew the day would come! No need to send out a trading expedition bristling with guns, eh? Better this way, isn't it?"

"Oh, yes," Fran said dryly. "Much better. Without the weight of guns you carry more cargo. Bigger profits."

"Always the warrior, aren't you? Tut, tut, Sir Francis! I really believe you'd rather have war than peace! I really believe—"

He was still delivering his little jibes when a mud-spattered messenger arrived. Sir Francis Drake was to come to London immediately! Philip had seized the corn ships and imprisoned the crews. Only one ship, the *Primrose,* had escaped. There was no doubt that the seizure of the corn ships was a piece of deliberate, intentional treachery. The *Primrose* had captured a Spanish official with orders from Philip of Spain in his pocket.

18

Admiral Drake in command

"The corn ships seized?" Mr. Chessley said. "No! Impossible!"

"Why impossible? Fran asked. "The corn ships weren't 'bristling with guns,' were they?"

"But it's unbelievable! When we were at peace—when we . . ." After a silence Mr. Chessley got up. "Sir Francis, we've said some harsh things about you. But that time is past! When you sail to avenge this dastardly crime, the merchants will be back of you! Every merchant ship in England will be yours if you want it! And you'll be in absolute command! Oh, that Philip of Spain! That fiend in human form! That . . ." He went out, still muttering.

"What does he think you'd want of merchant ships?" Elizabeth asked. "They can't fight, can they?"

"Dear, a merchant captain who couldn't fight wouldn't be afloat very long. Our merchant vessels always sail half-armed. When England needs them for battle, they just mount a few more guns and they're ready for action."

"And the merchants stop their trading—give up their profits—go to all the expense of outfitting their ships and paying their crews—just to help the Queen? That's very patriotic of them, isn't it?"

No use to tell her all the problems he'd face. That he must not only win his battles, but make the action pay for itself. That he must take prize ships, or capture cities and hold them for ransom, to pay the expenses of outfitting the fleet. That the men who sailed with him would be volunteers, depending on him for their wages. No use to tell her that. She'd worry enough about the shooting side of the fighting, without trying to understand his money problems.

"Yes, dear," he said, "our merchants are patriotic—when something wakes them up."

He kissed her, and ordered a horse brought around. He'd not be in London long, he said. He'd come back to Plymouth to ready his fleet for action.

When he returned to Plymouth in the *Elizabeth Bonaventure,* he had his commission: Sir Francis Drake, Admiral of the Fleet, was to destroy Spain's overseas defenses—from Santiago in the Cape Verde Islands to San Domingo in the Caribbean—from Cartagena on the Spanish Main to St. Augustine on the coast of Florida. Besides the *Elizabeth Bonaventure* he would have another of the Queen's ships, and twenty-seven merchant vessels. The biggest private fleet that had ever rallied to the flag of a commander. The merchants had honored him with their trust—and saddled him with problems.

The expedition would cost 60,000 pounds before it sailed. He knew he'd have to make good that cost, and pay the wages of the volunteers who sailed with him—2,300 men, including 1,000 soldiers.

Soldiers . . . another problem there. He saw the threat of trouble as soon as the fleet began to gather. From the first the mariners and soldiers stalked around one another like game cocks sizing up a rival's spurs.

Captain Carleill, in command of the soldiers, made it plain where he stood. "My men will be serving under me, Sir Francis, but I'll be serving under you! And if any soldier forgets that, he'll be reminded!"

They shook hands on it. Nearby, a soldier and a mariner, standing toe to toe, were hurling insults.

"When the time comes for action," Carleill said, "they'll pull together. All I hope is that we get to sea soon!"

"Yes," Fran said. "For more reasons than one."

He and Carleill didn't need to say what they were thinking. They both knew how many times Fran had gathered a fleet, waited in harbor with supplies wasting and men falling sick, only to get orders to disband the fleet.

"Surely this time," Carleill said, "the Queen won't change her mind!"

"I'll feel better when the last merchant ships get here," Fran told him.

The last ships had barely arrived when a letter came from London. Admiral Drake had better sail immediately, or his orders might be canceled! They sailed.

When they reached the Cape Verdes, Fran and Carleill planned the action. Carleill would go ashore with his troops, approach Santiago secretly by a wide detour, then fall on the city, capture it, and hold it for ransom.

The soldiers swaggered and taunted the sailors. "We're the ones who'll take Santiago! We're the ones who'll collect your wages for you!"

"Ahhhh!" a mariner snarled. "How'd you get here without us? Swim?"

The mariners were still hurling insults when the last troops went ashore. Then they were silent, and Fran knew that some who had jeered loudest were praying. Hour after hour their thoughts followed the march of Carleill's men. No sound of battle . . . So far, no ambush had taken the troops by surprise . . .

At dawn, the men on the ships stared in amazement. Not a shot had been fired, but the cross of St. George flew over Santiago. Fran went ashore to hear the news. The troops had found a ghost city. The people had fled to the hills, taking their treasure with them, leaving the empty houses to their fate.

When the fleet weighed anchor from the Cape Verdes, they left ruin behind them. The military results would rock Philip on his throne. But the financial results would worry England. Not a ducat of ransom.

If we don't do better at San Domingo, Fran thought, I'll have another price on my head.

The men were scowling. No ransom. How were they going to be paid? In a few days, though, they recovered their spirits. San Domingo would be different! Why worry about Santiago? Beastly place. Wouldn't live there if Philip gave it to them. Glad it was behind them. They didn't like the mosquitoes.

Fran listened and smiled. What a mixture they were! They'd face any danger without flinching, then grumble at a little thing like a mosquito.

A week out from the Cape Verdes the ship's doctor came to Fran. Some very sick men, he said. Chills and fever—violent pain—a lot of the men out of their heads. "So sudden, Sir Francis. I've never seen anything like it."

A cold knot twisted in Fran's stomach. "Do any of them . . . turn yellowish?"

"Yes, they do!" The doctor looked relieved. "Then you've seen it before? You know what to do? Thank God!"

"I've seen it. When I was in the Caribbean. But I don't know what to do. Nobody knows. A Spanish captain gave me one piece of advice. 'Be beforehand with the graves.' I lost more than half of my men."

"God in heaven, Sir Francis!"

In ten days more than two hundred men had died. Three hundred others were tossing and muttering. Those who had recovered from the fever lay around in a daze, blank-faced, with staring eyes.

When the ships anchored in the Caribbean, the captains gathered for a council. Did they have enough well men to attack San Domingo? Or should they wait until the sick had recovered?

Fran told them of the weeks at Hidden Harbor. "We'd better strike now, before any others fall sick."

They agreed.

He sent two pinnaces ahead to scout. "Try to pick up a pilot who knows the harbor of San Domingo. And try to make contact with the Maroons. There are supposed to be some in the highlands back of the city. We'll follow you as soon as we've careened and cleaned the ships. Look for us in a week."

"A week, sir?" one captain said. "You can't possibly—"

"We've got to."

A week later the fleet weighed anchor and sailed to overtake the pinnaces. The first pinnace had a Greek pilot who knew the defenses of San Domingo.

"Impregnable!" he declared. "It has never been captured." As he sketched the walled city and its defenses, it was easy enough to believe it had never fallen.

"Is there a place to land troops and march on the city?" Fran asked.

That was impossible, too, the pilot said. There was one landing place, ten miles west of the city. But very dangerous surf there. Only a man who knew the waters—

"If boats have landed there, my boats can!" Fran said. "I'll pilot them in, myself."

Even if they got through the surf, the pilot said, it would be useless. His men would go to their death. Guardhouses on the shore. Pickets stationed there every night. No chance to storm the guardhouses without spreading an alarm and rousing the countryside.

Fran said, "I see . . ." and waited for his other pinnace to report. It came with one Maroon on board, a slim lad who said his name was Pedro.

"I had a friend once named 'Pedro,' " Fran told him. "I shall call you 'Pedrito.' "

Pedrito's smile gleamed. He had heard of El Draque. He would be El Draque's friend. All the Maroons would be El Draque's friends. The pickets? El Draque need not think of pickets. There would be none in the guardhouses that night!

As soon as darkness fell the ships approached the landing place. Pedrito came to meet them in a canoe. Everything was ready for the landing.

"You trust him?" Carleill asked.

"If I couldn't trust a Maroon," Fran told him, "I'd be dead."

"If you're wrong this time," Carleill answered, "we'll be dead."

Pedrito did not understand English, but he must have felt the mood. "I have spoken the truth, El Draque! Your men will find no pickets! I will stay with you! My body will be a hostage for the truth of my words!"

"I don't need a hostage," Fran said. "You may stay as

my friend. When we take San Domingo, what do you want as a prize?"

"I get what I ask for?"

"If it's in my power to give it," Fran promised.

"Then I want to go with El Draque and be his man as long as I live!"

"You're my man!" And Fran went to the boat to pilot the first troops through the surf.

It was almost dawn when they put the last troops ashore. The fleet sailed east and took up a position before the city. Fran watched the sun. Now was the time—if he and Carleill had calculated correctly.

He ran out his guns, began a bombardment, then launched his boats, as though he intended to force a landing west of the city wall. He waited. Was the ruse going to work? If it didn't . . . The west gates opened, and the soldiers poured out to repel the landing.

Trumpets blaring, drums beating, Carleill's men swept down from the rear, and beat their way into the city. The Spanish—townspeople, officials, and soldiers—fled through the rear gate to the hills. Fran sent an ultimatum to the governor: 25,000 pounds, or he would destroy the city.

"While we're waiting," he told his officers, "take care of the shipping in the harbor. The galleys, first. Free every galley slave."

Tom Moone was one of the captains who boarded the galleys. After an hour he reported to Fran. "At first, I kept hoping I'd find some of our men, sir. Maybe some of the ones who went ashore from the *Minion*. Pretty soon, I began to hope I wouldn't find any of them. They'd be better off dead. Sir, those galley slaves—they're like animals. When we strike off their chains, they grovel like whipped dogs. They can't believe they're free."

"Tell them we'll take them to England, and then send them to their own countries if they want to go," Fran said.

No answer yet from the governor of San Domingo. They removed all guns from the defenses, and stowed them in the holds of their ships. Still no word. Then a watchman reported he'd had a glimpse of a group of horsemen approaching under a flag of truce.

"We'll send a messenger to meet them," Fran said.

"Please, El Draque!" Pedrito begged. "May I be your man?"

Off he marched, head high, a white flag fluttering on a staff. He disappeared up the winding road. In San Domingo they waited. At last they saw Pedrito returning. Slowly now, dragging his flag, one hand pressed to his chest.

"Pedrito!" Fran ran to meet him. . .

"Forgive me, El Draque, I . . . failed . . . you." Pedrito slumped in the road. His hand fell away, and his blood stained the dust.

The Spaniards, still under their flag of truce, came down the road.

"Which one of you violated the truce?" Fran asked.

"Who insulted us by sending a Maroon?"

Fran saw them through a red haze. "I'll not deal with you till the man who killed Pedrito is dead. What's more, I'll hang two of our prisoners in San Domingo every morning until you do surrender the knave."

The Spaniards protested. El Draque could not mean that! El Draque was known for his mercy to prisoners! He would not stain that reputation to avenge the death of a Maroon!

"I'll hang the first two in the morning at six!"

The next contingent of Spaniards who came down the road brought an officer stripped of his rank. "He is yours, El Draque. Execute him, and spare innocent men!"

"Hang him yourselves!" was the grim answer. "Then I'll receive the governor's answer."

The governor was ready to ransom San Domingo, but he could not possibly raise 25,000 pounds. One-fourth that amount was all. San Domingo no longer had the wealth of early days. The Indians had died off, and the Spanish did not have enough slaves to work the mines.

When the fleet sailed they left San Domingo defenseless, her harbor empty of shipping. But the action had not paid for itself. They sailed, and the fever sailed with them. They had conquered a city, but they had not conquered the fever. Unless the sickness ended, time was running out. They would lack the crews to man their ships, and troops to storm the cities.

They must strike next at the richest city in the Caribbean—Cartagena, Fran told his captains. It was the center of trade in pearls and gold. And they must capture it quickly, before time ran out. He knew something of the defenses of Cartagena from his time at Hidden Harbor. He explained the harbors to his captains by drawing a capital H. The left-hand upright, to the west, was the strip of land that enclosed the harbors. At the bottom, the outer harbor. At the top, the inner harbor, with a chain across the narrow channel between them, and heavy guns ready to bombard any ship that approached it.

As for the city—he drew a square on top of the H. That was Cartagena, facing south on the inner harbor. No landing place to the west. No way to land troops on the interior and march on Cartagena. A river and marsh cut her off from land to the north and the east.

Carleill put his finger on the left-hand upright of the H—the seaward strip of land west of the harbor. Was it possible to put troops ashore there, where they could march on the city?

Fran shook his head. Foot soldiers could be landed there. They could start their march up the strip. But they would not live to reach the city. A battery of guns covered the strip. Moreover, a deep barricade of poisoned stakes had been driven into the ground across the narrowest point of the strip.

"No approach by land, and no approach by water?" Carleill remarked. "Then it looks as though Cartagena *is* impregnable."

"Not quite," Fran said. "There is a way for troops to pass the poisoned stakes and rush the guns!"

That night the troops landed on the southern end of the strip of land, cut across it diagonally to the sea, and waded north in the surf, passed the barricade of poisoned stakes, and rushed the guns. Another "impregnable" city fell.

But once more the treasure houses were empty. A million pounds to ransom Cartagena? They could not pay more than one-tenth of that, the governor said. And once more the fever raged. Men had been dying by threes and fours. Now they were dying by dozens.

Fran called a conference with Carleill and his land captains. Should they accept the ransom offered? Or should they hold the city? Should they keep it as a base against Spanish power in the Caribbean?

"We can hold the city," Carleill said, "if you can guarantee that the Queen will keep a fleet in the Caribbean. If she will send ships, freshly supplied and manned, every few months."

Fran thought back over the last few years. "No, I can't guarantee that."

"Then it would seem wiser to us, sir," Carleill said, "to accept the ransom they've offered, and leave the Caribbean before the fever has destroyed us. And—one other thing—Sir Francis. The matter of pay. I've discussed it with my officers. We've all agreed on what we have to say about that."

That they deserve the lion's share of the spoils, Fran thought. He could not blame them for that. The action had been amphibious. Ships and land troops had both been vital. But he could not expect them to see that. Carleill and his men had made the attacks. Therefore . . .

"My captains and I have agreed, sir," Carleill said, "that we want no pay. We want our share to go to the poor men who have worked and fought with us—both the soldiers and the mariners. We only wish, for their sakes, it could be more."

Fran's voice was husky. "I've never been so proud to call men my friends."

"We hope we'll serve with you again, Sir Francis," Carleill said. "Perhaps, next time, for gain and glory, both. If not for gain—the glory will be enough."

A guard interrupted the meeting. "Sorry to break in, sir, but a sailor says he's got to see you, Sir Francis."

"Begging your pardon, sir," the sailor said, "but we thought you'd want to know. They—they got Captain Tom Moone, sir. He's dead."

19

Destination—Cadiz

Tom Moone dead! Carleill looked as shocked as Fran felt. "How did it happen?" Fran asked.

"We were taking over the ships in the harbor," the sailor said. "We didn't expect any trouble. They'd all struck their colors. This little frigate seemed to be deserted. No answer when we hailed her. But men were hiding, sir. And when we went aboard . . ." He stopped, bit his lips, and finally went on. "Captain Moone is ready for burial at sea, sir. We thought maybe you . . ."

Fran read the service over Tom, while the tough, hard-bitten crew stood at attention with stony eyes. He watched the body slide into the water, and felt as though a part of himself had died and been buried, too.

Back on the flagship he summoned his captains. "Free all galley slaves, then burn the shipping. Burn every vessel afloat in the harbor of Cartagena!"

"If any men are aboard?"

"Let them jump!"

"And leave them to drown?"

Fran glared. "No! Haul them out, and hold them prisoners. But burn the shipping. Don't depend on a surrender. Don't trust a Spaniard, even if he strikes his colors. Don't trust any Spaniard—ever!"

An hour later one of the officers who was freeing the galley slaves returned to the flagship. "Sir Francis, one of the slaves says he knows you. Wants to talk to you."

"What's his name?"

"He won't say. Just shakes his head. Either doesn't remember, or he's pretending he doesn't. All he'll say is, 'Talk to El Draque, please.' "

"Then bring him here."

The officer hesitated. "There's one other thing, Sir Francis. We think he's a Spaniard. And you said—"

"I said bring him here!"

"He may be up to something, sir."

"I doubt if a galley slave has any love for Spain."

"He might love forty thousand ducats, sir. That's the current price on your head, isn't it?"

"Bah! Bring him here!"

"Aye, aye, sir. Soon as we wash him. He stinks like a fox. They all do."

Four officers brought the man—two flanking him on each side. They were tall fellows, but the white-bearded man towered over them. He was naked to the waist, and, though his weather-beaten body was skeleton thin, his shoulders were massive. His huge hands could have wrung their necks as an ordinary man might wring the neck of a chicken.

"You wanted to see me?"

"*Sí, señor.*" His voice was a husky whisper, as though perhaps he had lost the habit of speaking.

"You are Spanish?"

"My parents were Spanish, *señor*. As for me—it is hard to say. I have been long in the galleys, *señor*." He turned, and Fran saw the scars on his back. He faced Fran again. His sunken eyes were searching. Then, as though satisfied with what he found, he nodded. "The little *señor* has come a long way. It come true, what I tell you a long time ago. Remember, *señor*? I say, 'You will be a better master than Adam Tanner.' "

"Pedro!" Fran was on his feet, striding toward him.

The huge hands reached out to grip Fran's shoulders. "Remember how we say good-by, *señor*? I say, 'Go with God, my friend.' You say, '*Vaya con Dios, amigo.*' "

"It's all right," Fran said to the officers. "He's an old friend of mine."

"Sir!" one protested. "He's admitted he's Spanish!"

"My parents were," Pedro said. "Even though they were driven out of Spain when they were children. When Spain banished all Jews and Moors. They loved the land. They talk of it to me. They say, 'Some day, you get to go home.' It was true. I was in Spain. I was in Cadiz Harbor. *Sí*. I enter Cadiz Harbor—as a galley slave."

"What crime put you in the galleys?" one officer asked.

"A very black crime, *señor*. I was a sailor on an English ship. The whole crew was sent to the galleys."

"What can we do for you, Pedro?" Fran asked.

"Let me serve you, *señor*. Protect you, night and day. I think El Draque, the curse of Spain, maybe going to need protection."

After a few days the crew had grown used to the towering figure that stood by Fran's door when he slept, and behind Fran's chair when he ate. They glowered sometimes, they measured him with sidelong glances, but they said nothing.

When the fleet entered Plymouth Harbor, they carried the guns of Santiago, San Domingo, Cartagena, and St. Augustine in their holds. They had rescued a starving English colony at Roanoke. They had wreaked havoc on Spanish defenses. The price, though, had been high. A third of their men. Less than a hundred lost in battle. More than six hundred dead of the fever. And—what Fran knew would hang over his head—the expedition had not paid for itself. Fran sent a report to London, then went to Buckland Abbey to await his summons.

"Oh, Fran!" Elizabeth whispered, "Thank God you're back! I couldn't go through these last months again if—"

"You get used to it, *señora*," Pedro told her cheerfully. "War or peace—he always be in danger. Always be somebody after his head. But you have my promise, *señora*. No matter who try to kill El Draque—on land or sea—he have to kill me first!" He bowed and left them alone.

"What did he mean?" she asked. "War or peace, you'd be in danger?"

"Nothing, dear. Just—nothing, really."

"I think," Elizabeth said, "that you'd better tell me a lot of things. All those things you keep from me so that I won't worry."

"But—"

"Otherwise, don't you see? I'll be worrying about what I don't know."

"Now, dear—"

"Start talking, *señor!* Or I'll ask Pedro!"

He talked.

"So," Elizabeth said, "if it's war, they'll send you to fight. If it's peace, your head may be the price."

"Try to have as much faith in me as the Spanish," Fran suggested. "They think it would take a magic bullet to kill me."

Soon he went to London to answer for the financial failure of the expedition. But neither the merchants nor the Queen's council talked much about the cost. They were too concerned over the latest news from Spain. Santa Cruz, Philip's greatest admiral, was getting ready to invade England. Assembling a vast *Armada*—an armed fleet. Sir Francis must help them plan their defense against it.

"The only defense is attack," Fran said. "We must destroy the eagles before they hatch. Destroy them in their nests. We must destroy the Armada in the harbors of Spain!"

The Queen protested. It was madness to think of taking a fleet away from the coast of England. They must have every ship there for protection. It was weeks before Fran could persuade her. At last she signed his commission.

Sir Francis Drake would sail to prevent the gathering of the Armada. He'd have four of the Queen's ships this time—the *Elizabeth Bonaventure,* the *Golden Lion,* the *Dreadnaught,* and the *Rainbow,* and two of the navy's pinnaces, the *Makeshift* and the *Spy*. Fran promised to outfit four vessels of his own. The merchants of London and of the Levant Company would provide the others.

Elizabeth did not protest when she heard the news. "When do you sail?" was all she asked.

"In March—I hope," Fran said. "If I were two people, I'd be surer of that. Then one of me could be in Plymouth, organizing the fleet, and the other could stay in London, to argue with the Queen if she begins to waver."

By March the most of his fleet was ready. The ships of the Levant Company had not arrived. Storms and contrary winds were delaying them. A message from London warned Fran. The Queen was on the brink of changing her mind. To strike at the coast of Spain, she was saying, that might bring on war. Perhaps it would be better just to have the fleet stand by in the Channel, ready to protect England. Perhaps . . .

Fran waited for the Levant ships. Waited . . . while supplies wasted and men began to fall sick. Waited . . . praying each day the Levant ships would get there before his orders were canceled. At last, on April 1, the Levant ships arrived. A rough trip, they reported. Before they sailed, they'd need time to—

"We weigh anchor in the morning!" Fran roared.

He drew his first easy breath in weeks when the coast of England sank below the horizon. His relief didn't last long. Off Cape Finisterre a storm rose. It raged for five days. Another five days passed before the fleet was together again.

"Our rendezvous is Cadiz!" Fran said. "Pass the word!"

He sat in his cabin with Pedro, discussing the harbor of Cadiz. It was like a capital B, turned over, Pedro said. The upright was the narrow isthmus along the Atlantic coast. The loops of the B were the two harbors.

The isthmus was low and sandy part of the way, then high and rocky to the north, where the city of Cadiz rose sheer from the sea. The northern loop of the B was the outer harbor, and the southern loop was the inner harbor. A narrow channel between them. Everything well protected, Pedro said. Batteries of cannon on the rocks above. Reefs and shoals in the water below. And oared galleys in the harbor. Very big ones, manned by hundreds of slaves.

"We'll need a west wind to enter," was all Fran said.

When the rocky precipice of Cadiz was off their larboard bow, only part of the fleet was together. Some of the merchant ships were lagging far behind. But the wind was from the west, and Fran called his captains for a hasty conference.

"We'll stand into the harbor now, while the wind is fair."

Captain Borough, his Vice-Admiral, in command of the *Golden Lion*, said, "Sir Francis! I must protest!"

"You *what*!"

"It's madness to take sailing vessels into a harbor protected by oared galleys! It's against every rule of naval strategy to—"

"Rules! Bah! We're going in!" Fran got up. "That's all, gentlemen!"

"But what is our plan of battle?" Captain Borough asked.

Fran shrugged. "How do I know? This is no court dance, that follows a pattern."

"But we must have orders, Sir Francis! We must—"

"You only need one order! Follow me! And when you get inside, destroy the shipping!"

They stood in toward the harbor. It opened before them, and they saw the mass of shipping. At least three vessels for every one of theirs. Two large galleys sped out to meet them. A raking broadside stopped the galleys, and the fleet entered Cadiz Harbor.

Ten galleys bore down on them. One broadside from the Queen's ships broke the attack.

"Wonder what old Captain Borough thinks of his 'rules of naval strategy' now?" Fran muttered.

A panic of fleeing ships filled the harbor. The galleys and some small vessels took refuge behind reefs and shoals, where the deeper draft vessels could not follow them, and where the shore batteries protected them. Others fled to the inner harbor. By sunset, of eighty vessels in the outer harbor, the English had captured or burned thirty-seven.

The *Golden Lion* hailed the *Elizabeth Bonaventure*. Should Captain Borough lead the way out of the harbor?

Fran didn't bother to explain his next plan. Why hear another lecture on naval strategy? "Come to anchor!" he ordered, "and don't move unless I do!"

All night his fleet rode at anchor unmolested. At dawn he organized a flotilla of the little pinnaces and some of the ships' boats, went through the narrow channel to the inner harbor, making straight for a huge vessel anchored there. A galleon being built for Santa Cruz, himself. She was not ready for sea, so they set her afire and spent the morning beating off all attempts to rescue her. By noon she was beyond saving. Fran piloted his little flotilla back to the outer harbor.

What the devil was going on? The *Golden Lion* and some of the merchant vessels were standing out of the harbor. What "rule of naval strategy" was old Borough obeying now?

Rules! Bah! Fran returned to his flagship and gave the

signal to weigh anchor. Then, suddenly as a fog would roll up in the Channel, the wind died, and every sail hung limp. They were becalmed in Cadiz Harbor.

Action all around them now. Troops poured onto the low land of the isthmus, dragging guns over the sand. Galleys massed for another attack. Across the harbor—where the turn of the tide would sweep toward them—the Spanish were readying fireships.

"*Por Dios!*" Pedro whispered. "They have us now!"

"Not while my ammunition holds out," Fran said.

He battered the gun emplacements on the isthmus first, until the troops scattered. The attack of the galleys came next. They never got within range of the fleet.

Night fell. Not a breeze stirred. Then, on the turn of the tide, the fireships blazed and came driving toward the huddle of motionless English vessels.

But the boats that went to meet them were from Fran's own ships, and manned with Devon lads. Every fireship was turned off her course, to drift on shoals, go aground, and burn.

At two o'clock in the morning—they had been becalmed for fourteen hours—a breeze rose, and the fleet sailed. The fireships were still blazing. Half the shipping in the harbor had been destroyed or taken prize.

"We've made a start," Fran said. "We've singed the beard of the King of Spain. God willing and the wind with us, we'll finish the job!"

The winds were not with them. Once more a gale

forced them to claw off a lee shore. When the fleet reassembled some long-faced captains confronted their commander. They could not keep the sea much longer, they said. Too many men sick. They must return to England, where they could clean their foul ships, and—

"We'll send the sick men home on the prize ships," Fran said, "and careen our fleet here."

But there was no possible refuge where they could—

"Bah! Half a dozen harbors handy. We'll take Cape St. Vincent. Good, strategic location. While we careen and trim part of the vessels, the others can harry the Spanish shipping."

Captain Borough had been shocked before. He was horrified now. Cape St. Vincent was absolutely out of the question! The guns of Sagres Castle protected it. And Sagres Castle was impregnable. A wall enclosed two hundred acres on a rocky promontory. On three sides, cliffs two hundred feet high. On the fourth side, a passage only two hundred feet wide up to the gate. There was no way to bring their heavy guns to bear on Sagres Castle.

"Then we'll take it without our heavy guns," Fran said. "That's all, gentlemen."

Captain Borough departed speechless. But presently a boy brought a long letter of protest. The attempt to storm Sagres Castle was madness. In the first place . . .

Fran sketched through the letter, stormed off to the *Golden Lion,* ordered Captain Borough arrested, put Captain Marchant in charge of the ship, stormed back to the *Elizabeth Bonaventure,* and summoned his land captains.

"The way to breach that gate," he said, "is to burn it."

The captains were silent.

"Well, gentlemen?"

Sir Francis was in command, they said. They would obey. But had he counted the cost in lives if they—

"Have you counted the cost in lives if we don't careen and clean our ships?" he asked.

"You are in command, Sir Francis," an officer said. "It is your right to send our men—"

"*Send* them? I'll lead them!"

20

Disowned

Captain Marchant came ashore where the soldiers were forming for the attack on Sagres Castle. He saw Fran shoulder a bundle of fagots. "Sir Francis! What in the name of heaven?"

"We're going to burn the gate."

"But you—if anything happened to you—"

"You'd be in command," Fran said.

They charged the hill, piled pitch and fagots against the gate, and lighted them. The flames leaped. Their musketeers kept up a steady fire at the loopholes of the fort. An hour passed. The flames had done little damage to the gate. Two hours . . .

"We'll be here this time tomorrow," a soldier muttered, "if any of us live that long!"

Suddenly the Spanish sounded trumpets for a parley. Their commander was dead. They were ready to surrender. The harbor of Cape St. Vincent was in English hands.

The men cheered, but the captains were still shaking their heads. Nothing but a miracle had saved them.

"Even a miracle wouldn't have saved us," Fran said, "if we hadn't secured a place to careen our fleet." He divided the fleet into squadrons. While one group was in port, the other continued raiding. By the time the whole fleet was shipshape again, they had destroyed more than fifty vessels laden with supplies for the Armada.

Captain Marchant came to Fran. "Sir Francis, there's a plot under way. One of our men has been sneaking ashore, conniving with the Spaniards. We've been keeping an eye on him for days."

"Who is it?"

"Pedro. We've seen him talking to the same men five different times."

"Probably collecting some information," Fran said.

"I don't know about information," Marchant said dryly, "but today he collected some money. Quite a handful of ducats."

"You think he's being paid to kill me?"

"What else can we think?"

"Just a handful of ducats? Come, come! I'm worth more than that!"

Someone knocked, and Pedro's voice called, "*Señor?* May I see you? Quickly, please? Very important!"

"Sir Francis, don't!" Marchant urged.

But Fran called, "Come in, Pedro!"

Pedro entered, glanced down at Marchant, bowed, and held open the door for him. "You going out, *señor*?" It could have been a question—or a suggestion.

"I stay," Marchant said.

"*Sí, señor.* I not be long." He reached into his pocket and laid a handful of ducats on the table before Fran. "Mine. Paid to kill you. What you think?"

"You've been cheated."

Pedro grinned. "Oh, this not the whole pay, *señor.* I been arguing about that for days. They say forty thousand ducats. I say fifty thousand. After what you do to Cadiz Harbor, you ought to be worth more, eh? But I tell them I would wait for my pay till a treasure ship reach Spain—if it not be too long. And you know what they say, *señor?* In less than a month a treasure ship—she come. The *San Felipe*. Big like the devil—fifteen hundred tons! So—pretty quick—the *San Felipe* be at San Miguel in the Azores, eh?"

"Pedro, you're a military genius!"

"No, *señor.* Just a little bit bright. Even a dumb man—he know this expedition not pay for itself yet. The men—they are getting long faces. We take the *San Felipe,* they feel better, eh?"

The merchant captains were not in favor of going after the *San Felipe.* How could they be sure they'd find her?

San Miguel, in the Azores, was eight hundred miles off shore. What if they missed the *San Felipe?* Another month, at heavy expense, and nothing to show for it.

Fran let them talk. When they stopped, he said, "Our rendezvous is San Miguel."

One day out from Cape St. Vincent a storm scattered

the fleet. It raged for three days. When it died, only nine ships answered the signal guns of the *Elizabeth Bonaventure*—the other naval vessels and Fran's four.

"Think it's any use to wait for the merchant vessels?" Captain Marchant asked.

"Our rendezvous is San Miguel. They may meet us there."

"If they don't?"

"We'll take the *San Felipe* without them."

Two days later they sighted a sail off their starboard bow, well to the north. Not big enough to be the *San Felipe*. Another treasure ship, homeward bound from the Azores?

Fran sent the *Golden Lion* and the *Spy* to challenge her.

After a time his lookout reported, "The *Spy* is returning sir, but not the *Golden Lion!*"

They came about and waited for the *Spy*. Captain Marchant was aboard her. He came to the flagship to report.

"The ship was one of our merchant vessels," he said. "She refused to rejoin the fleet. Mutinied, sir. And the crew on the *Golden* Lion mutinied, too. They were going home, they said. They gave me my choice. I could go to England in command, or in irons. I demanded to be set aboard the *Spy*. I deserted my command, Sir Francis, but I did not desert my commander!"

"Welcome aboard," Fran said. "And there'll be a few

necks stretched when we get back to England!"

Ten days out from Cape St. Vincent . . . twelve . . . fourteen. No sign of the *San Felipe.* Had they missed her? Fifteen days. If they didn't take a prize, they'd be on mighty short rations before they got home! How much longer, Fran wondered, could he hold them to their purpose? Nine ships in his squadron now, and every morning when he went on deck he checked to be sure that he still had nine. The morning of the sixteenth day the pinnaces were lagging far behind. Deserting? He ordered the *Rainbow* to put back and wait for them.

Only the *Elizabeth Bonaventure,* the *Dreadnaught,* and his four little vessels now. They stood to the west.

"Sail ho-o-o-o! It must be the *San Felipe,* sir! Biggest ship I ever saw!"

Yes, Fran thought, if reports were true, she was the biggest ship any of them had ever seen. His six ships put together did not equal her fifteen hundred tons.

He summoned his captains. "We have two things in our favor. The weight of our guns, and our power of nimble steering. We must get to windward of the *San Felipe,* and keep the weather gage. We'll attack in a single line. I'll lead, and you others will follow. That way, each ship can bring her full broadside to bear. We'll pass her on a starboard tack, come about, and pass her on a larboard tack. Always keeping in that line ahead, so every ship can use her full broadside."

When the *San Felipe* was close enough for the men on

deck to see her, they stood for a moment as though frozen, staring at her.

But Fran was swaggering about, calling cheerily, "Gently, my lads! We don't want to sink her! We're going to take her back to England. If one of you gunners does too much damage, I'll make him plug the holes, himself!"

They laughed, but the sound died in their throats. They looked again at the towering sides of the mighty vessel.

The *Elizabeth Bonaventure* led the way, and the others followed, pouring their broadsides into the *San Felipe*. Nimble steering and heavy gunnery won the day. The pride of Portugal's East Indian fleet struck her colors.

When Fran checked the papers of the *San Felipe*, he knew his troubles were over. Her cargo was worth twice the cost of the expedition. There would be no question now about turning him loose again! The Queen would send him back, with fresh ships and crews, to finish what he had begun. And she must send him back! He had played havoc with Cadiz, but he had not touched the shipping in Lisbon. Unless he could smash that shipping, too, he had not stopped the Armada.

But the Queen's eyes were cold, and her words were harsh. "You go too far! I sent orders to Plymouth, forbidding you to enter Spanish ports or to land on Spanish soil!"

Thank heaven I got away when I did! Fran thought. He said, "I must have been at sea before the orders came, Your Majesty."

"We have apologized to Spain for what you did."

"Your Majesty!"

"Let us hope Philip accepts the apology. If he does not, you have driven us to war."

"Your Majesty, we *are* at war! I've won the first skirmish, but it's only a beginning! I must go back as soon as I gather a fleet! I must—"

"You'll not go back! Go home to Devon and stay! Unless you'd prefer to go to the Tower!"

The council were silent. They did not protest. They would not look at Fran.

Lord Burghley came to see Fran before he left London. "Regrettable," he said. "Regrettable. The Queen is making a great mistake. Playing right into Philip's hands. Giving him the one thing he needs most. Time to get ready for the invasion!"

"Then tell her so!"

"It's no use, Sir Francis." He sighed. "A baffling situation. You—our greatest commander—after the greatest campaign of your career—a perfect campaign—and you are—"

"In disgrace?"

"I'd not put it quite that strong, Sir Francis, but—"

"Let me know when you think of the right word," Fran growled. "I'll be at Buckland Abbey." And, meantime, he told himself, I'll collect a few facts and figures for Her Majesty. One man to Spain, to check on Santa Cruz, Another to the Low Countries, to check on Parma, Philip's leader there. Santa Cruz and Parma will plan this action together. With Parma right on our doorstep . . .

Lord Burghley must have been reading his mind. "And don't risk any private scouting, Sir Francis. It would get back to the Queen, and I tremble to think what would happen to you."

"Yes, Your Lordship. I understand."

The first day in Buckland Abbey he sat with Pedro and Elizabeth, laying his plans.

"Give me a fast pinnace, *señor,*" Pedro said, "and I go to Spain."

"You know the risk you'll run."

Pedro shrugged. "It is nothing, *señor.* I be as safe in Spain as you be in England. One little slip—a dungeon for me and the Tower for you, eh? Don't worry, *señor!* I save our necks—both of them. When I come back—I have the facts!"

On a fine, foggy night in July he sailed. August passed. September. October. In Flanders, the Spanish envoys talked of peace. In the harbor of Lisbon, Fran knew, Santa Cruz was gathering his Armada. Why didn't Pedro come? Surely he'd have been back by now—if he was ever coming.

It was mid-November when Pedro returned. "I get the facts, *señor!*" The Armada would have 150 ships, 8,000 mariners, and 2,000 galley slaves. And that was only the beginning. For the land action after they had invaded England they would carry 20,000 soldiers with complete equipment. Cannon for land service, and mules, horses, and carts. All told, more than 32,000 men, with supplies for six months.

Fran put the information in a letter to Walsingham. He added information about Parma's doings. Odd, he said, that while Spain talked of peace, Parma had built boats to carry 2,000 horses, and had 200 ships ready to transport 50,000 men.

"What will happen?" Elizabeth asked, "When the Queen knows what you've been doing?"

"Maybe we give a big feast while we wait?" Pedro suggested. "Might be the last one for a while."

The Queen's answer was a summons. Sir Francis Drake would appear before the Queen's council! Immediately!

The Queen was shocked. She had received secret information, she said, that Philip still planned to invade England! Sir Francis must plan their defense against the Armada!

"Our only defense is attack, Your Majesty. We must destroy the Armada before it weighs anchor. Give me a striking force of thirty sail. Supply my ships so I can keep the sea. Feed my men and feed my guns, and I'll stop Santa Cruz without losing a ship!"

It took weeks to persuade the Queen, but at last Fran returned to Plymouth in triumph, aboard his flagship, the *Revenge*. Once more his drum beat through Devon, and ships and men rallied to the call. By March he would be ready to put to sea. By April he'd be . . . In February, Santa Cruz died. The Queen ordered half the fleet in the Medway disbanded, sent peace commissioners to Flanders again, and rushed off orders to Plymouth. Sir Francis Drake would please stand by. On no condition must he sail. He must do nothing to disturb the peace negotiations!

Again Fran sent spies to scout the Spanish preparations, and Parma's doings. He waited through March, while supplies were consumed and ships long in harbor grew foul. He waited while men sickened, and had to be dismissed and replaced. Waited.

His spies returned. Philip had appointed Medina Sidonia to command the Armada. It would sail any day now. In the Low Countries, Parma was poised to strike. Once more he risked the Queen's displeasure by sending information to London.

Another summons. Sir Francis Drake was to meet with the Queen, her council, and Lord Howard, the Lord Admiral of England.

"What battles has Lord Howard won?" Elizabeth asked. "Why aren't you Lord Admiral of England?"

"I can't be. I'm a commoner."

"I'd be prouder of a knighthood I'd earned myself than a title handed down to me!" Elizabeth declared.

Fran grinned and kissed her. "But it doesn't qualify me to be Lord Admiral."

"It just qualifies you to go to London and tell them what to do?"

"That's it."

"Suppose you'll keep your temper?"

"I have to." He held up his right hand. "I promise!"

At Lord Howard's first words, Fran almost broke his promise. They must be ready to defend England, Lord Howard said. And since they could not know whether the Armada would strike by way of Ireland, Scotland, or the Channel ports, they should break the fleet into three units, and—

How many times had he said it? How many more times would he have to say it? "Your Majesty, and Your Lordships! Our only hope now is to attack the Armada with every sail we can muster! Excepting for a small force to keep Parma bottled up in the Low Countries, we must sail to meet the Armada with every ship we have!"

"And leave our shores unprotected?" Lord Howard asked.

"Why worry about our shores if the Armada never gets here?"

Lord Howard shook his head. "What if the Armada eludes us? No, we must have strength to protect our shores."

"From what?" Fran asked.

"From the Armada, you fool!" the Queen shrieked.

Fran counted to ten and started over again.

At last Lord Howard nodded. "Sir Francis, I agree. I propose that we assemble our combined fleets in Plymouth, and sail for Spain!"

"When we're provisioned," Fran said. "We've got to be

ꝑp the sea. And every ship needs three times
.pply of ammunition. The way we'll use our
, our powder and shot wouldn't last two days."

Before Fran left London the council had abandoned the divide-and-defend plan. They were ready for a unite-and-attack maneuver. Ninety-four ships assembled in Plymouth Harbor. Now, as soon as they had enough supplies to keep the sea . . .

But sufficient supplies did not come. Instead, they got word that the Armada was at sea. What to do?

"Sail while the wind's with us," Fran suggested, "and hope we contact the Armada before we starve!"

They sailed. But the wind veered, and held them prisoners in the Channel for seven days. They put back. They waited two weeks for supplies. They sailed again. Once more the wind veered, and they returned.

The third time they were revictualing the fleet when the wind blew fair. Lord Howard ordered the supply ships they had not unloaded to follow them, and sailed. This time they reached the mouth of the Channel before a southwest wind stopped them. Word from a scouting pinnace. A storm had battered the Armada. It was in the harbor of Corunna.

Corunna! With a fair wind they could get south of Corunna in two days! They'd have the weather gage of the Armada! Any wind that blew fair for the Armada would be blowing fairer for them!

This time, they were out three weeks before the winds

drove them back. Once more the fleet, storm-battered, heartsick, returned to Plymouth.

Day after bitter day they worked. Cleaning the ships, dismissing the sick, caring for the dying, burying the dead. Combing the countryside for extra food. A week later, by Friday, June 19, they were half supplied, but still windbound. Word from London. More supplies were on the way. Of course, the southwest winds might delay them . . .

"For tuppence," Fran roared, "I'd go after them and show them how to sail!"

Lord Howard smiled. "I can't spare my Vice-Admiral to convoy supply ships, Sir Francis. How about a game of bowls?"

His officers stared.

"After all," Lord Howard said, "what can we do? Until the wind blows fair, we can't get out of the harbor. Besides, I believe it would put heart in our people to see us playing at bowls."

Fran smiled. Perhaps Lord Howard was not an experienced mariner, but he was a born leader!

A crowd gathered around them on Plymouth Hoe to watch the game.

Fran was standing, with a bowl in his hand, when Captain Fleming came racing toward them yelling, "That Armada! It's in the Channel!"

21

The Armada

"The Armada!" Captain Fleming shouted again. "It's in the Channel! Off the Lizard! I never saw such a fleet! Spread out on a front seven miles wide!"

The Armada in the Channel. The English fleet windbound in Plymouth Harbor. Fran could feel the shock of the news hit the crowd. He heard them gasp. He saw their eyes turn—not to the Lord Admiral of England—but to El Draque, who had been at war with Spain so many years.

Windbound in Plymouth. My words, he thought, are coming home to roost. How many times had he shouted that a fleet in harbor was at the mercy of the fleet outside? And now the people were remembering. He could see it in their faces. One wrong move on his part, and the townspeople would panic. They would flee inland in terror, away from the threat of the Armada. They would leave harbor, town, their work, everything.

And the crews . . . How did one pour courage down this rat hole?

He whispered to the man nearest him. "Sound the drums! Roust them out! Get every man on board!"

Nobody noticed when the man scuttled away, for Fran was shouting, "That so, Captain Fleming?" And his shout was a taunt. "That so? Well, I'm going to finish my game. Time enough for that, and to beat the Spanish after!"

He made quite a thing of sizing up the ninepins, then with a relaxed swing he released the bowl and prayed it home. It toppled every ninepin.

Some of the crowd laughed, some cheered, and some were muttering. But nobody was fleeing in panic. Five minutes would finish the game. Of all the ways I've ever poured courage in men, he thought, this is the oddest!

The crews were going to need courage. He knew the long, backbreaking hours ahead of them. They were going to have to warp the fleet out of Plymouth Harbor. Slavery for the men in the boats. They would have to carry the ships's bow anchors out ahead of her, and let them sink. Slavery for the men at the capstans, too. Tramping round and round, reeling in the cable, dragging the ship up to the anchor. And the whole thing to do over again and again. For ninety-four ships.

Galley slaves under a lash never worked harder than their men would work this night. Brutal toil for men in condition. For their disheartened, half-starved crews . . . But it had to be!

Meantime, four men, with a nation's fate in their hands, finished their game. Then the Lord Admiral, Vice-

Admiral Drake, Rear-Admiral Hawkins, and Captain Martin Frobisher marched off to the harbor.

By nightfall, only eight ships had been warped out of Plymouth.

"Due west," Fran told their leader. "Work up to westward, hugging the coast."

"If Sidonia sees us?"

"That's the idea!" Fran said. "He must see you! Don't worry my lad. He won't stop for you. He'll think you're the vanguard of our fleet. All that escaped from the harbor. He'll press on, to catch the rest of us windbound."

"I hope so, Sir Francis!"

Eight ships, with lanterns burning, stood to the west.

When the short summer night ended only forty-six other ships had escaped the harbor. Forty were still trapped, waiting to take on supplies, waiting for men to complete their skeleton crews.

The forty-six sailed straight across the Channel, toward France. When they were far enough south to hope they had given the Armada a wide berth, they stood to the west. Forty-six ships, short of men, of supplies, of ammunition, were leaving the coast of England unprotected, on the chance that they could weather the Armada.

Late Saturday afternoon the lookouts sighted the Armada. The English thanked God for a drizzling mist, and lay to under bare poles. With no sail spread they might escape detection. If the Spanish did not see them, if the Armada passed on until it was east of them, if the wind still held from the southwest . . .

Sunday morning Fran shouted, "We've done it! We've won the weather gage!"

"Maybe that's all we'll win," someone muttered.

Fran gave no sign he had heard the man. He could not blame him for what he was thinking. The Armada—the famous eagle of Spain—with a wingspread seven miles wide—was an appalling sight. A strong vanguard leading the way, the supply ships massed in the center, protected by wings of fighting ships and a strong rear guard.

And, beyond Dover, Parma waited with more ships and fifty thousand men. Between the Armada and Dover every Channel port of England was exposed. Not enough fire power anywhere to stand against even one wing of the Armada.

No hope for England but in her ships—those that had escaped from Plymouth. It was up to them to hound Sidonia up the Channel, past every port, and to prevent his juncture with Parma. But how? They had the weather gage—unless the wind changed; they had their fire power —unless their ammunition gave out.

The vanguard of the Armada changed course. Was Sidonia going to attack Plymouth, where forty ships lay helpless?

The English fleet heeled over on the port tack and bore down on the right wing of the eagle. Time and again they came about and repeated the maneuver. They battered the division so fiercely that at last the vanguard turned aside from Plymouth to come to the aid of the right wing.

When the action ended they had driven the Armada beyond Plymouth. That harbor was safe. What next? What harbor would Sidonia threaten now? The Isle of Wight? That was the best harbor ahead of him.

Lord Howard summoned the captains of his council. They planned. They must harry the Armada past Portland and the Isle of Wight. But they would need their full force to do it.

They waited off Plymouth that night until the other ships cleared the harbor and joined them. Then they organized the pursuit of the Armada. Sir Francis Drake would lead them, Lord Howard said. The rest of the fleet would follow his stern lantern.

No sleep for Fran that night. He was on deck in the darkness, listening for any sound. Would Sidonia take a lesson from the English fleet? Come about in the dark, give them a wide enough berth to elude them, and tack to the west until he had the weather gage?

One o'clock in the morning. Fran blinked his eyes and shook his head to clear the fog. When had he had more than a snatch of sleep with both ears cocked? The minutes dragged. Two o'clock. The moon rose, and he saw what he had feared—ships beating their way westward! One—two—three. Was it the vanguard of the Armada?

Or the rear guard? Was Sidonia just starting his maneuver? Or had he already weathered them?

"Put out the stern lantern and come about!" he ordered.

His master was dazed. "But we're leading the fleet, sir! What will they do when our lantern—"

"They'll stand by, you idiot! The orders were to follow my stern lantern. If it goes out, any fool should know enough to wait until he sees it again!"

Shortly before dawn the *Revenge* overtook the ships. Only three German merchant vessels, wholly unaware of what they had passed in the night. Fran muttered under his breath, and gave the order to rejoin the fleet.

Then, in the dawn, they saw her—the great Spanish galleon, *Our Lady of the Rosary,* disabled and left behind by the Armada. The *Revenge* bore down on her.

"Strike your colors!"

Fran heard drums beating to quarters on the crippled ship. Don Pedro de Valdez, her captain, had courage! He could not possibly maneuver his ship. Her bowsprit and foremast were both shot away. But he was ready to go down fighting.

"Who are you?" Don Pedro called.

"El Draque! And I'm in a hurry! Strike, or I'll send you to the bottom!"

Don Pedro struck his colors. He and his chief officers came aboard the *Revenge.* It was an honor, Don Pedro

said, to surrender to El Draque, the greatest commander in England.

Don Gregorio, one of the younger officers, was not taking their defeat so gracefully. He shot a lowering look at El Draque, and sang a taunting song under his breath. It was in Spanish, but Fran could translate:

Bartolo, my brother,
To England forth is gone,
Where The Drake he means to kill . . .

Fran smiled to himself. His reputation had gone up and down in England from year to year. He seemed to keep it better in Spain. “What will you do to Lord Howard?” he asked.

Don Gregorio paused. “Who’s Howard? Never heard of him.” He went on with his song.

Fran sent a prize crew to the ship. “Bring off any treasure,” he ordered, “then repair her and take her to Dartmouth.”

The men brought off a chest with fifty thousand ducats, and a dozen whips, made of cord and wire.

“We can’t figure out what these are for, Sir Francis,” one said. “Not as long as the whips they use on the galley slaves. But they’re carrying hundreds of them.”

“Those whips,” Don Gregorio said haughtily, “will be used to flog heretics. It won’t matter that we’ve lost a few hundred. We have thousands more in the other ships. When we invade England—and we will—we’ll flog to death all heretics over seven.”

Fran waited until the red haze in front of his eyes had faded. “Bring me some more of them. I’d like about a hundred.”

Don Gregorio’s eyes widened.

Fran spoke softly, through his teeth. “Don’t worry. I’m no Spaniard. We’ll not use the whips. I want them as gifts for our captains. As reminders, in case any man forgets why we’re fighting.” Maybe, he thought, when I can’t feed my men and my guns—when my men are hungry and my guns are silent—maybe the sight of those whips will help my men hang on!

The *Revenge* spread every sail and sped east to rejoin the fleet. The breeze grew fitful and began to die. The *Revenge* had barely overtaken the fleet when she was becalmed. Fran called for a boat and went to the *Ark* to report. John Hawkins and Martin Frobisher were with Lord Howard.

As Fran entered, Frobisher jumped to his feet. "What the devil happened to you?"

Fran glanced at Frobisher, then past him, and reported to Lord Howard.

"You left us in a devil of a mess," Frobisher said. "When your light went out, what did you expect us to do?"

"Stand by and wait for another signal, of course! I had to be sure the Armada was not getting the weather gage of us."

"I say you deliberately put back to take that prize!" Frobisher declared. "And you should be brought to trial for deserting your post. And if I don't get a share of that prize, I'll have some of the best blood of your belly!"

"But if you do get a share of the prize," Fran asked, "then it's all right? And I don't need to be hanged? Is that it?"

"Gentlemen!" Lord Howard was quietly crisp. "Sir Francis has explained himself. His action did result in confusion, but—"

Fran shrugged. "I knew there was that possibility. If some headlong fool didn't obey orders, and went on without the signal light. But—" He saw Lord Howard flush, and a glint of anger in his eyes. Uh-oh! So Lord Howard had been the "headlong fool" who had failed to stand by! Fran waited for the explosion.

But after a moment Lord Howard spoke quietly. "As I said, some confusion resulted. But that is past. We are together again, and the Armada is before us. That is our problem."

"Have we got more ammunition yet?" Fran asked. "No? Then by tomorrow night we'll have another problem."

Tuesday they prayed for more powder and shot, and spent what they did have in savage fighting. They knew they were taking a toll of lives on the crowded Spanish ships. But they were not destroying the Armada.

Toward evening Lord Howard had to signal to discontinue the engagement. They were dangerously low on ammunition.

That night they cheered when ships came racing from English harbors and hailed the *Ark*. Powder and shot at last! But it was only some eager volunteers, wanting to join the fleet. Just give them ammunition, the masters said, and tell them what to do!

"If they'd get ammunition for us, and then stay out of the way . . ." Fran suggested.

Lord Howard smiled wryly and nodded. "Let's hope the sight of our reinforcements will worry Sidonia. I'm afraid that's the only help they'll be. In heaven's name, why doesn't ammunition come!"

All night, with every vessel that hailed them, they hoped again. Just more volunteers, ready to join the fleet—if they could get ammunition.

Ammunition arrived Wednesday—again just enough for a day and a half of action, at the rate they were spending powder and shot. With the supply came a warning. The Tower could not send more. The fleet must not waste it. England needed a reserve on hand for defense, in case Sidonia's forces did land.

"Defense!" Fran raged. "Don't they know yet that our only defense is attack?"

All that day, and until afternoon on Thursday, they were becalmed. Then, for a few hours, the wind rose, and they pounded the weather flank of the Armada with savage broadsides. When the action ended they had driven Sidonia beyond the Isle of Wight—but they had "wasted" a lot of powder and shot to do it.

Friday—another calm. On the *Ark* Lord Howard knighted six of his commanders for their valor in battle. John Hawkins was one of them.

"Not only for your valiant action during this battle, Sir John," Lord Howard said, "but for a far greater service that you have done for England, in building up our fleet. The superb condition of our ships gives the lie to every charge that your slanderers have leveled against you. I have said as much in dispatches to the court, and I'll keep on saying it, until all England knows your worth!"

Fran wrung John's hand, and hoped Lord Howard's words would heal part of the heartbreak of the long struggle.

Saturday—a wind. The Armada, still in formation, sailed on. Gusty squalls prevented fighting, but they dogged the heels of Sidonia's ships. When they drove him through the Strait of Dover, though, he'd have the weather gage of Lord Seymour's squadron that was blockading Parma. They sent a fast pinnace to warn Seymour. By nightfall Seymour had beaten his way west through the strait and joined them.

That night the Armada anchored off Calais. The English came to anchor, too, still keeping to windward of Sidonia. Somehow—without spending too much powder and shot—they had to dislodge him, break his formation, and drive him past Dunkirk before he joined Parma.

The commanders gathered with Lord Howard. Fireships. That was the way to do it. No time to collect derelicts. They'd have to use some of their own vessels.

Fran's squadron was anchored to starboard of the fleet, nearest the Armada, so they chose most of the fireships from his vessels. They spend the day loading them with pitch, brimstone, and fagots, and priming all their guns.

Toward evening they sent a pinnace to scout the anchorage of the Armada. Well anchored, the captain reported, and lying rather close together. But they covered a mighty long front. Eight fireships weren't going to do very much damage.

"Have you ever been at anchor on a lee shore," Fran asked, "when fireships came blazing down on you out of the dark?"

"No, Sir Francis."

"Then you can't begin to imagine the damage that eight fireships can do!"

The commanders gathered on the *Revenge* to watch the maneuver. Volunteers from Devon made up the crews of the fireships—just enough men to set them on their course, and light the fires. Each fireship trailed a boat at her stern for the escape of the crew.

Midnight . . . one . . . one-thirty. A half hour of slack water, then the flood set in—the flood that would pour through the anchorage at Calais.

The fireships sailed in the darkness. Presently they blazed and their cannon roared, as though some demons of the underworld lived on the blazing decks and manned the guns. What a roaring inferno was bearing down on the Armada! Lord Howard and his commanders shook hands and waited to greet the returning volunteers . . . and waited.

No sign of the boats coming back from the fireships. What had happened? Had the men failed to escape after they started the fires? Had they lost the boats they towed? Had they gone overboard from the blazing, decks, only to be drowned in the racing current?

22

[illegible]

[illegible]

22

The winds of heaven

The sand in the hourglass ran out, and the quartermaster turned it. Still no sign of the volunteers. The commanders looked at one another, heartsick.

From the water a cheery hail. "Ahoy, the *Revenge!*" The grinning volunteers came aboard.

"We followed after the fireships for a bit," one said, "to watch the fun."

What a panic! Such yelling and screaming! Every ship cutting her cable to get away in a hurry. Ships crashing into one another. Oh, it was a magnificent mess. That was the end of the Armada! They wouldn't have to worry about Sidonia any more!

But the commanders knew it was only the beginning of the end. The action tomorrow would be the most vital battle of the whole time. They must drive the Armada to leeward of Dunkirk.

The next morning they sailed east through the Strait of Dover, and saw Sidonia's ships. For the first time the

Spanish ships were scattered in every direction. But the rigid command and organization of the Spanish fleet were still effective. Sidonia was beginning to rally his forces. The victory was not yet won. They must drive the Armada beyond the junction with Parma—and do it before their ammunition ran out.

"No long bowls today," Fran ordered. "We've got to make every shot count."

An hour of the hottest combat of the week. Two hours. They were driving the Spaniards on—inch by inch. But they were spending their precious store of ammunition round by round. Three hours . . . four . . .

Were they going to have to retire from the fight, and lose the victory for want of ammunition?

The battle raged for eight hours before a sudden squall stopped it. When the rains ceased, Lord Howard's ships drew off. No need to waste the last of their precious powder and shot. A northwest wind was going to finish the battle for them. It was driving the Armada on the Zeeland Banks. Tomorrow, it would all be over. The Armada aground and helpless. Nothing to do but accept their surrender.

But the wind veered, and the Armada—that had seemed doomed—was free, and fleeing to the north.

Once more a conference on the *Ark*. "How much ammunition have you, Sir Francis?" Lord Howard asked.

"I couldn't stop a longboat."

It was the same story from every commander.

"Then," Lord Howard said, "we'll have to put on a brag countenance, won't we? Keep after them as though we could fight. And pray to heaven that the wind doesn't veer and give them the weather gage."

Fran returned to the *Revenge.*

"What we do, *señor*?" Pedro asked.

"Keep Sidonia from turning back," Fran growled. "What with—I don't know."

Pedro's grin was cheerful. "That's easy, *señor.* The *Revenge,* she do it alone! She got El Draque!"

Fran smiled briefly. If their "brag countenance" did not fool Sidonia . . . if the Armada turned back and challenged them . . . if they were forced to flee from her . . . if they were caught between the Armada and Parma's forces . . .

But Sidonia did not turn back. The Armada continued north, and turned west around Scotland. No need to pursue Sidonia farther. They could leave the Spanish to the winds of heaven—and the lee shores of Scotland and Ireland.

They had some hint of how the winds of heaven had served the Armada when a few battered ships were driven back into the English Channel. Less than one-third of Sidonia's fleet would ever reach home again.

The Invincible Armada had failed. Philip of Spain would not come ashore as a conqueror on the one little island that was England.

It was weeks before Fran got back to Buckland Abbey. Elizabeth was waiting with shining eyes. "Oh, Fran, I'm so proud of you! So proud! If only I could have been with you in London when you saw the Queen! If only I could have heard her—"

Before Fran could stop him, Pedro spoke. "El Draque, he got the devil, *señora.* The Queen—you know what she say? Why we not capture some prizes? How is England going to pay for this battle? That what she want to know!"

"Fran! He's joking!"

"Afraid not," Fran said. "After all, the country has been to very heavy expense. No . . . I'm not very popular in London just now."

"Do you know what I'm going to do some day?" Elizabeth stormed. "Some day—hundreds of years from now—my ghost is coming back! I'm coming back, just to see what people are saying about you then! After they realize how much you've done for England!"

Fran smiled. "Better not, dear. Your ghost wouldn't like it. You know what people will be calling me? A pirate. It does sound so exciting."